RADIO
PROJECTS

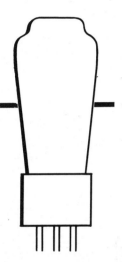

Abraham Marcus

Englewood Cliffs
PRENTICE-HALL, INC.
1955

ACKNOWLEDGMENTS

The following manufacturers were kind enough to furnish photographs, or components to be photographed, to help illustrate this book:

P. R. Mallory and Co., Inc.

Precision Apparatus Company, Inc.

Sylvania Electric Products, Inc.

Thordarson-Meissner Manufacturing
　　Division of Maguire Industries, Inc.

United Transformer Company

To them, my warmest thanks.

ABRAHAM MARCUS

· ·

CONTENTS

INTRODUCTION

One of the most gratifying experiences in radio is that of building your own set. When you build a set yourself, you see the practical application of your theory. It is for this reason that this project book has been written as a companion for *Elements of Radio* * and *Radio Servicing, Theory and Practice.***

The organization of this project book follows that of *Elements of Radio.* Starting with the construction of the simple crystal detector receiver, it proceeds through the diode receiver, triode regenerative receiver, and tuned-radio-frequency receiver up to and including the present-day superheterodyne receiver. On the way you learn how to eliminate batteries and to replace the cumbersome headphones with a loudspeaker. As has been noted in *Elements of Radio,* these are the steps by which the science of radio developed historically.

Although this project book is designed primarily for use with *Elements of Radio* and *Radio Servicing,* there is no reason why it can not be used with any other beginner's book. Each project has been time-tested and all "bugs" have been removed. Explanations are clear and should be understood easily.

Attention is called to the type of construction employed in this book. It has been the custom to have beginning radio projects constructed on "breadboards"—that is, on a flat piece of wood upon which all the components are mounted. Here, such construction has been avoided for a number of important reasons.

First of all, it produces a messy and confusing end-product which, after the wiring is completed, resembles nothing so much as a plate of spaghetti. As a result, the beginner comes away with no realization of the precision and accuracy required in radio construction.

Secondly, such a construction entails lengthy leads, and hence it is quite difficult to avoid unwanted feedback due to the inductance and capacitance between leads. This may make it impossible to get some of the projects to operate properly.

Thirdly, practical radio receivers do not employ breadboard construction. Hence the resulting projects do not resemble anything with which you are likely to have practical contact.

In this book, regular chassis construction is employed. The components are mounted above and beneath a metal chassis, just as in ordinary commercial receivers. Wiring is neat, leads are short, and the projects have a professional appearance.

The chassis presents the most difficult problem, since most readers will not have the equipment required to form it. Ideally, each project should be available in kit form, using

** Abraham Marcus, *Radio Servicing, Theory and Practice,* 2nd Edition. (New York: Prentice-Hall, Inc., 1954.)

* Abraham and William Marcus, *Elements of Radio,* 3rd Edition. (New York: Prentice-Hall, Inc., 1953.)

a stamped and drilled chassis and components to match. All one need do, then, is to assemble and wire the project.

Where such kits are not available, however, it is possible to make your own without too much difficulty, as a glance at the photographs in this book will show. The top of each chassis consists of a piece of sheet iron of about #25 gauge. Each sheet is six inches in length, and the width varies from 4 to 7½ inches, depending upon the project. The side pieces that support the top are made of ½-inch wood, 6 inches long and 1½ inches high. The front and back pieces may be made of bakelite or wood about ⅛ inch thick and 1½ inches high. The length of these pieces will vary with the width of the chassis. All wooden pieces should be well sanded and painted. The chassis is held together by means of ½-inch wood screws.

Socket holes are cut in the metal sheet by means of socket-hole cutters. Other holes are drilled with an ordinary hand drill. Components are fastened to the chassis by means of machine bolts and nuts.

Each project (except Project #1, which teaches the beginner how to solder) follows the same outline. First there are references to pages in *Elements of Radio* and *Radio Servicing* where material pertinent to the project is to be found. You are urged to make full use of these references.

Next comes a general discussion concerning the project, followed by the circuit diagram for the project. It would be well to copy these circuit diagrams. By doing so, the beginner becomes familiar with the various symbols used in radio and, more important, he can see more clearly how the various components are connected to each other.

Then follows a list of the apparatus and materials required for the project, and after this, photographs showing top and bottom views of the project. These photographs are important because they show you how the components are laid out on the chassis.

Next, there is a descriptive list of all the new components used in the project, with their symbols. Each such component is illustrated in a photograph and explained and described in the text. This list is followed by instructions for constructing the project. Finally, there is a section dealing with the testing and operation of the project. In the course of testing and operating these projects, you are introduced to the voltmeter (for measuring the voltages produced by the power supplies of Projects #5 and #6) and to the signal generator and output meter (for aligning the tuned-radio-frequency tuner of Project #8 and the superheterodyne receiver of Project #9).

Note the wide range of subjects covered by this project book:

Receivers (simple crystal, diode detector, regenerative detector, tuned-radio-frequency, superheterodyne); *amplifiers* (radio-frequency, intermediate-frequency, audio-frequency); *oscillators* (radio-frequency, audio-frequency); *tubes* (diode, triode, r-f pentode, beam power pentode, pentagrid converter, multiunit); *power supplies* (power-transformer type, transformerless half-wave type employing selenium rectifier, transformerless ac-dc type); *heater circuits* (heater operating from step-down transformer,

v

heater employing a voltage-dropping resistor, series-connected heaters); *automatic-volume-control circuits; manual-volume-control circuits; tone-control circuit; inverse feed-back circuit; alignment of tuned-radio-frequency receiver; alignment of superheterodyne receiver.* Inasmuch as many users of this book will go on to become licensed amateurs, a code oscillator has been included as one of the projects (Project #10) to enable you to learn the Morse code, as required for such a license.

You should have on hand the following tools and supplies:

Soldering iron (about 100 watts), together with a spool of rosin-cored solder, a can of non-corrosive soldering flux, a sheet of #00 sandpaper, a small quantity of #00 steel wool, several clean rags.

Hook-up wire, solid push-back type. One spool each of red and black.

Insulating spaghetti. One spool each of red and black.

Hand drill, and a set of metal drills from $\frac{1}{16}$ to $\frac{1}{4}$ inch.

Pliers. One 6-inch combination type, one 5-inch long-nose type, one 5-inch diagonal cutting type.

Screwdrivers. One with $2\frac{1}{2}$-inch blade, one with a blade $\frac{1}{8}$-inch wide and with a long shaft and an insulated handle.

Hex nut drivers. For $\frac{1}{4}$-inch, $\frac{5}{16}$-inch, and $\frac{3}{8}$-inch hex nuts.

Rule. One foot.

Try square. Six inch.

File. Ten inch, fine cut.

Hammer.

Center punch.

Colored pencil. Red or blue.

One or more sets of the following tools should be available for use:

Set of chassis punches (such as the Greenlee type) for cutting holes. To cut holes $\frac{3}{4}$, 1, $1\frac{1}{8}$, $1\frac{1}{4}$, and $1\frac{3}{8}$ inches in diameter.

One $\frac{3}{8}$-inch and one $\frac{1}{2}$-inch metal drill, each mounted on $\frac{1}{4}$-inch shaft.

One $\frac{17}{32}$-inch, open-end wrench for use with the chassis punches.

Hand reamer. $\frac{1}{8}$- to $\frac{1}{2}$-inch holes.

Hacksaw, with blades to match.

Cold chisel, 1-inch, with metal block or anvil.

Pair of tinner's shears.

In addition, at least one each of the following instruments should be available:

Multimeter (such as Precision Model 120).

Signal Generator (such as Precision Series E-200-C).

#1

HOW TO SOLDER

GENERAL INFORMATION

In radio construction, most of the connections between the various components are made by means of wire leads. These leads must make good electrical contact with the terminals of the components. If we were merely to wrap the wire ends around the terminals, the wires would soon pull loose. Even worse, oxidation and corrosion by the air would coat the metal surfaces, thus interfering with the electrical contacts. Accordingly, after making a good mechanical connection between the wire and the terminal, we coat the joint with a layer of solder that keeps the contact firm and prevents oxidation and corrosion by the air.

Solder is an alloy of lead and tin, generally composed of about equal amounts of each metal. When it is heated (by a soldering iron or some similar device), it melts, at a temperature of about 400° Fahrenheit. The liquid solder flows over the joint and, upon cooling, hardens in place. (Actually, the molten solder melts a slight portion of the metal with which it comes in contact and the two liquids combine chemically. However, the metallurgy involved is quite complicated and will not be discussed here.)

Three things are necessary if you are going to obtain a good soldered joint. The first is *cleanness*. The surfaces of the metals to be soldered must be absolutely clean. This means that these surfaces must be scraped clean to the bare metal with a knife, file, steel wool, sandpaper, or other suitable instrument.

The second requirement is the use of a *flux*. This is a chemical that prevents the metal surfaces to be soldered from oxidizing as heat is applied. If a coating of oxide forms, the solder will not stick. (It is for this reason that it is so difficult to solder to aluminum. To do so, special fluxes and procedures must be employed.)

There are a number of different fluxes that may be used for soldering copper and iron. For radio work a non-corrosive flux, such as rosin, is employed. This rosin may be in the form of a paste that is applied to the clean surfaces that are to be soldered or, more commonly, the solder wire itself may have a rosin core. As the wire is heated, the rosin melts first and flows over the joint.

The third requirement is *heat*. The metals that are to be soldered must be made hot enough so that, when the solder is applied to the joint, the solder melts and flows easily. There are a number of methods for heating these metals.

SOLDERING DEVICES

The most common device for heating the metals to be soldered is the electric soldering iron. It consists of a wooden handle, a heating coil inside a metal barrel, and a copper tip that extends into the barrel. When electric current flows through the heating coil, the copper tip is heated. This tip is placed on the joint to be soldered and supplies the necessary heat. An electric cord through the handle carries the current from the power outlet to the heating coil.

Electric soldering iron

The heating ability of the soldering iron is rated in watts. Where the surfaces of the metals to be soldered are large or the objects are massive, a high-wattage iron is required. For ordinary radio work, however, an iron of about 100 watts is adequate.

Where electricity is not available, the soldering iron can be heated by other means such as a gasoline blow torch or a gas flame. The soldering iron then consists of a copper tip mounted at the end of a metal rod set in a wooden handle.

Another popular device is the electric soldering gun. The body of the gun is a plastic housing for a step-down transformer operating from the power line. The soldering tip forms part of the low-voltage, high-current secondary winding. As the trigger of the soldering gun is pressed, current flows through the transformer and through the soldering tip, which is made of a high-resistance metal. The high current, flowing through the high-resistance tip, quickly heats it sufficiently for soldering.

The soldering gun has a number of advantages over the ordinary soldering iron. It heats up faster (in a matter of seconds) and cools off just as fast. This is a boon to servicemen who, when they work in a customer's home, must first wait for the soldering iron to heat up and then for it to cool off sufficiently so that it may be safely packed away. Also, the soldering gun draws current and is heated only when it is in use. The soldering iron is plugged in and heated for the duration of the entire job. Some guns are equipped with low-voltage flashlight lamps that illuminate the job being performed.

Electric soldering gun

Heat is transferred from the tip of the soldering iron to the work to be soldered. Accordingly, the end of the tip must be shaped properly as shown below. The tip shown at A is used more frequently because it provides a larger contact surface between the iron and the work to be heated. The tip shown at B is used in smaller work where there is not enough room to insert a wide-tipped iron.

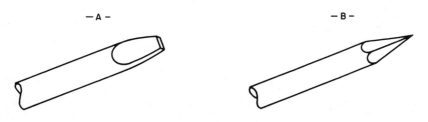

Shapes of tips of soldering irons

When the copper tip is heated, it oxidizes and a scale of black copper oxide forms over its surface. This scale interferes with the transfer of heat from the tip to the work. Accordingly, after the tip has been filed to the proper shape, it is *tinned*—that is, it is covered with a coat of solder. To do this, the iron is heated for about ten minutes. The copper oxide coat that forms on the tip is cleaned off with fine sandpaper. Flux and solder are immediately applied to the tip, the molten solder is spread over its entire surface, and the excess is wiped off with a clean rag.

If, in the course of work, the solder coat wears off, the tip must be retinned. If the tip becomes badly pitted, it must be refiled and retinned.

SOLDERING

The surfaces to be soldered must be cleaned down to the bare metal. If two wires are to be soldered, wrap them around each other. If a wire is to be soldered to a terminal, wrap the wire around the terminal. Make the joint as strong, mechanically, as possible. Remember, it is not the function of the solder to give the joint its mechanical strength.

If a paste flux is being used, apply it *sparingly* to the joint. When heated, the flux melts and spreads over the entire surface. After the joint has been soldered, the excess flux should be wiped off with a clean cloth.

If a rosin-cored solder is used, the flux melts first and flows over the joint. The excess flux is evaporated, as is indicated by the smoke produced as the work is heated. If any excess remains, wipe it off.

Apply the flat side of the tip of the soldering iron to the joint being soldered and hold it there only long enough to perform the soldering operation. The junction is heated until, as the solder is applied to it (not to the tip), the solder melts and flows freely over the joint. Hold the soldering iron in place for a few seconds more to evaporate the excess flux, then lift it away from the work.

The joint must be undisturbed until the solder hardens and sets, a matter of a few seconds. If the soldering was performed correctly, the joint should be covered with a smooth, shiny coat of solder. If the solder coat is dull and rough (this is called a "cold joint"), the joint should be reheated and, if necessary, some more flux added. If the joint still is improper, separate the work, clean the surfaces, and repeat the entire procedure.

After the soldered connection has cooled sufficiently for handling, it should be tested. First, make sure that you do not have a "rosin joint." In such a joint the metal surfaces are held together by the rosin flux, which is quite sticky, instead of solder. This may result if not enough heat has been applied to melt the solder and have it flow over the joint. You can test for such a joint by trying to pull it apart. (But proceed gently, lest you damage the terminal of the component being soldered.)

Next, wriggle one of the wires leading to the joint to see if the soldered surfaces are loose or adhere to each other. (Again, proceed gently so as not to damage any component.) If the wire feels loose, resolder.

Clean up any drippings of flux. Also, remove any excess solder that may have dropped down among the surrounding components. Keep in mind that neatness and cleanliness are not only the sign of a careful workman, but may make the difference between a successful and an unsuccessful project.

EXERCISES

Caution. Handle the hot soldering iron with care. Also, avoid spattering the molten solder.

1. *Soldering a wire to another wire.*

Tin the soldering iron, as described above. Scrape clean the surfaces of the wires that are to be joined. Wrap the wires around each other to make a good mechanical joint. Apply a small amount of flux paste to the joint. Heat with the soldering iron until the solder melts and flows over the joint. Remove the iron. Wipe off excess flux and remove any solder that may have dropped down.

2. *Soldering a wire to a terminal lug.*

Clean the wire and lug. Wrap the wire around the lug to make a good mechanical joint. Apply a small amount of flux paste. Heat the joint until the solder flows smoothly and freely. Remove iron, wipe off excess flux, and remove excess solder.

3. *Soldering a wire to an iron chassis.*

The iron chassis often is cadmium-plated to resist corrosion. Because of this plating, soldering becomes easier. When cleaning the surface of such a cadmium-plated chassis, use fine sandpaper and be careful not to remove the entire plate. Clean the surface of the chassis where the joint is to be made. Apply a little flux paste. Heat the spot with the soldering iron until the solder melts and flows freely. (Because the chassis conducts away the heat, it may be necessary to hold the soldering iron in place longer than for the other types of joints.)

After the spot on the chassis has been covered with solder, clean the end of the wire that is to be attached to it. Apply a little flux paste and hold the wire against the spot of solder on the chassis. Heat both wire and chassis with the soldering iron and apply more solder. After the solder has melted and covered both the wire and chassis, remove the soldering iron, but hold the wire firmly in place until the solder cools and hardens.

After all three types of joints have been made, test them by pulling on the wires firmly, but gently, so as not to damage any of the components. Also try wriggling the wires. When you are satisfied that the joints have been soldered properly, show them to your instructor for his approval.

PROJECT **# 2**

CRYSTAL DETECTOR RECEIVER

REFERENCES

Elements of Radio, 3rd Edition. Pages 19-99.

Radio Servicing, 2nd Edition. Pages 88-92, 94-97, 108-113, 204-214.

GENERAL INFORMATION

Although the crystal set of this project is the simplest type of receiver, it contains the four essential parts of all receivers—the aerial-ground system, the tuner, the detector, and the reproducer. An external antenna and ground are needed for the crystal set. This antenna may be of the type described on pages 26 and 27 of *Elements of Radio* or, even simpler, an insulated wire about 75 or 100 feet long may be used. One end of the wire is attached to the antenna post of the receiver and the wire is spread across the floor or lowered through an open window and permitted to rest along the side of the building. Be sure that the free end of the wire is insulated.

The ground wire is connected to the ground post of the receiver at one end and to any grounded object, such as a cold-water pipe or the metal plate of an electrical outlet, at the other. Be sure that the wire makes good electrical contact with the grounded object. The antenna and ground, together with the primary winding of the antenna coil (L_1), from the aerial-ground system.

The tuner consists of the antenna coil and the variable capacitor (C_1). The crystal detector is a fixed germanium type (see Figure 27-29, *Elements of Radio*). The reproducer is a pair of headphones.

6

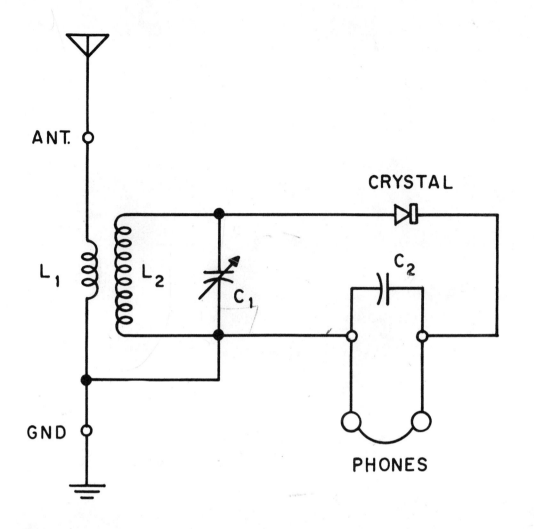

ANT.

L₁

L₂

C₁

GND

CRYSTAL

C₂

PHONES

Circuit Diagram for Project No. 2

APPARATUS AND MATERIALS REQUIRED

C_1—Midget 0.000365-μf variable capacitor
C_2—0.002-μf fixed capacitor (mica or tubular-paper type)
Crystal—1N34 fixed germanium type
L_1
L_2 } Antenna coil (Meissner #14-1004, or equivalent)
1 Pair headphones (2,000 ohms, or higher)
1 Dial plate (0-100)
1 Large bar knob
2 Binding posts (Antenna and Ground)
2 Tip jacks (for headphones)
Chassis—6″ x 4″ x 1½″
Miscellaneous hardware (2 single tie lugs, woodscrews, machine bolts, nuts, washers).

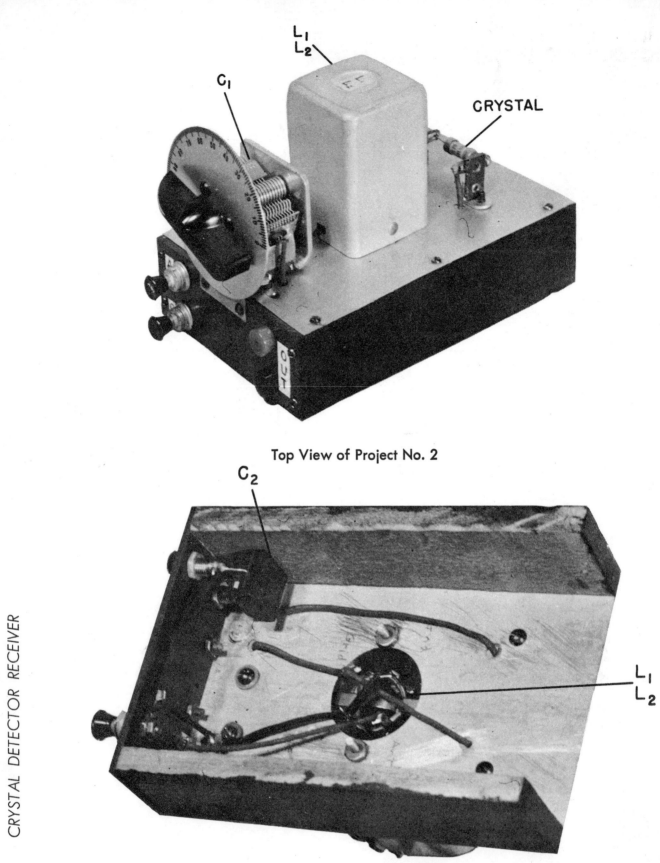

Top View of Project No. 2

Bottom View of Project No. 2

COMPONENTS USED IN THIS PROJECT

Symbol   *Explanation*

Variable capacitor

The variable capacitor consists of a set of stator plates and a set of meshing rotor plates. The curved line of the symbol usually represents the plates connecting to ground (the rotor plates).

Tubular-paper fixed capacitor

The fixed capacitor consists of metal plates separated by an insulator, or dielectric. In the tubular-paper type the metal plates are sheets of aluminum foil and the dielectric is waxed paper. This sandwich is rolled up, wrapped in a cardboard jacket, and impregnated with wax to make it moisture-proof. Wire leads, extending from each end, make contact to the metal plates.

Mica fixed capacitor

In the mica type, alternate layers of metal plates and mica sheets (the dielectric) are sandwiched and enclosed in a bakelite case. Alternate metal plates are connected together to form two sets. Wire leads connect to each set of plates.

Ceramic fixed capacitor

In the ceramic type, the metallic plates are printed upon opposite sides of a ceramic wafer that acts as the dielectric. The whole then is covered with an insulating plastic material.

The curved line of the symbol usually indicates the grounded set of plates. Fixed capacitors are rated according to the voltages at which they can safely operate. Thus you may see imprinted on the capacitor "400 v DCW" or "400 v d-c working." This means that this capacitor may be used safely where the voltage across it does not exceed 400 volts direct current. Some mica-type capacitors are color-coded to indicate their values and ratings. (See Appendix 1 at the end of the book.)

The crystal consists of a small piece of germanium and a thin wire touching a spot on it. The whole is enclosed in a ceramic tube.

Fixed crystal, type 1N34

The antenna coil consists of primary and secondary windings on a bakelite tube. The ends of each winding are attached to soldering lugs. The entire unit is mounted in an aluminum can which acts as a shield.

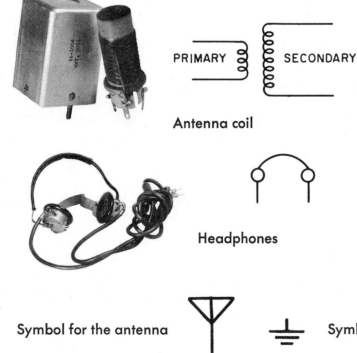

PRIMARY   SECONDARY

Antenna coil

The headphones used for radio reception usually have a resistance of 2,000 ohms, or more.

Headphones

Symbol for the antenna

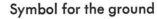

Symbol for the ground

CRYSTAL DETECTOR RECEIVER

CONSTRUCTION

Carefully examine the photographs of the project to plan your layout of components on the chassis. Keep in mind that a proper layout is one where the connecting leads are as short as possible. Before starting your construction, sketch your layout on a sheet of paper and show it to your instructor for his approval.

Then mark the centers of all holes on the chassis. Use a center punch and hammer to mark these centers. (In this way your drill will not slip when boring the hole.) Be sure to make all holes through which wires pass large enough so that the insulation will not be cut on the sharp edges of the hole. The hole beneath the antenna coil may be cut with a socket punch.

Mount all components on the chassis. On a separate sheet of paper, copy the circuit diagram. Then, as you make each connection, indicate it on this copy, using a colored pencil. In this way you can tell at a glance which connections have been made and which are still to be made. (It is well to use this procedure in all subsequent construction too.)

Make the connections between components as indicated by the circuit diagram. Be sure you make the proper connections to the antenna coil. When soldering the crystal and fixed capacitor in place, do not use the soldering iron any longer than is necessary for the connection. Otherwise, the heat may ruin the component. It is a good idea to hold the lead between the component and the soldered joint with a pair of long-nosed pliers. In this way some of the heat along the lead is conducted away from the component. (This procedure, too, should be used in subsequent construction.)

TESTING AND OPERATION

· Check your wiring to see that all connections have been made properly. Also check each soldered joint. Then show your project to your instructor for his approval.

To operate your set, connect the antenna, ground, and headphones. Mount the phones on your head and rotate the tuning knob slowly, starting at one end of the dial and proceeding to the other. Make a note of the position on the dial where each station you receive attains its maximum volume. Note that the lower the frequency of the station, the more completely the rotor plates of the variable capacitor are meshed in the stator plates.

PROJECT #3

DIODE DETECTOR RECEIVER

REFERENCES

Elements of Radio, 3rd Edition. Pages 100-107, 187, 188.

Radio Servicing, 2nd Edition. Pages 97-101, 118, 119, 214-217.

GENERAL INFORMATION

In this project a vacuum-tube diode replaces the crystal of Project No. 2. Except for this, the two projects are essentially identical. (It should be noted that modern receivers generally employ diode detectors.) Note that this project employs a 6H6 tube which contains two diodes in one envelope. For our purposes, both diodes have been connected in parallel, thus forming, in effect, a single diode. Of course, it is also possible to use only one of the two diodes.

The 6H6 tube requires 6.3 volts on its heater for proper operation. There are a number of methods for obtaining this 6.3 volts, but here we have used a line-cord resistor to drop the line voltage to the required 6.3 volts.

DIODE DETECTOR RECEIVER

12

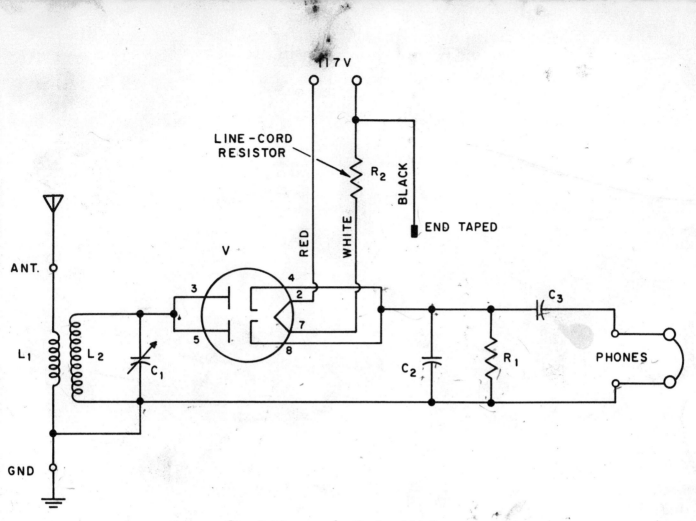

Circuit Diagram for Project No. 3

APPARATUS AND MATERIALS REQUIRED

C_1—Midget 0.000365-µf variable capacitor

C_2—0.0001-µf fixed capacitor (mica type)

C_3—0.01-µf fixed capacitor (tubular-paper type)

$\left.\begin{array}{l}L_1 \\ L_2\end{array}\right\}$ Antenna coil (Meissner #14-1004, or equivalent)

R_1—250K-ohm, ½ watt, fixed resistor

V—6H6 duo-diode tube

1 Line-cord resistor, 350 ohms (R_2)

1 Pair headphones (2,000 ohms, or higher)

1 Octal socket (MIP type, or equivalent)

1 Dial plate (0-100)

1 Large bar knob

2 Binding posts (Antenna and Ground)

2 Tip jacks (for headphones)

Chassis—6" x 4" x 1½"

Miscellaneous hardware (2 single tie lugs, woodscrews, machine bolts, nuts, washers).

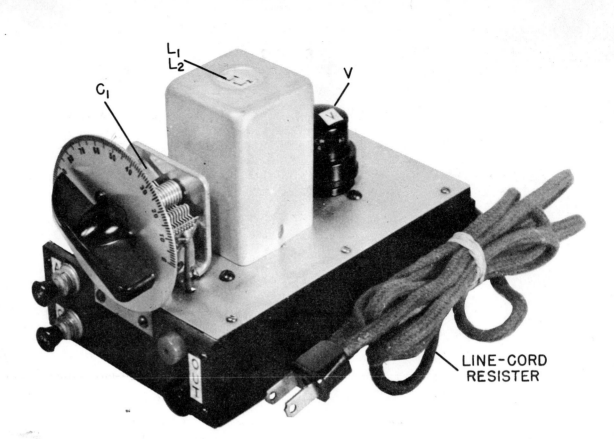

Top View of Project No. 3

Bottom View of Project No. 3

COMPONENTS USED IN THIS PROJECT

Symbol *Explanation*

Fixed resistor

Fixed resistors generally are of the wire-wound, carbon, or composition types. High-value resistors are generally of the carbon or composition types. In these projects, unless otherwise stated, resistors are of the carbon or composition types.

Fixed resistors usually are color-coded so that their values may be identified. (See Appendix 2 at the end of this book.) Fixed resistors are also rated according to their current-carrying capacities ($\frac{1}{2}$ watt, 1 watt, etc.).

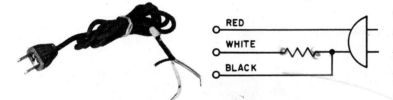

Line-cord resistor

Line-cord resistors are used to drop the line voltage to that required by the heaters of the tube or tubes. One end of the cord terminates in a plug that is inserted in the power outlet. The other end terminates in three leads—one red, one white, and the other black. In this project only the red and white leads are connected to the heater of the tube. The bare end of the black lead must be taped to prevent a short circuit. The line-cord resistor should never be cut.

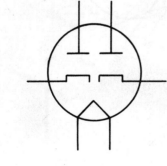

6H6 tube

The 6H6 tube consists of two diodes contained in a single envelope. Its base is an octal (8-pin) type, although only seven pins are used. The pins of octal-base tubes are numbered from one to eight (although all the pins may not be present).

Octal base

Octal socket

To identify the pins, hold the tube with its base towards you. Note the projection on the bakelite centering pin. With this projection facing down, the tube pin immediately to the left of the projection is pin #1. Proceeding in a clockwise direction, the next pin is #2, and so forth, counting all pins, even those that are missing.

For the 6H6 tube, pin #1 connects to the metal shell, pin #2 is one end of the heater, pin #3 is the plate of diode #2, pin #4 is the cathode of diode #2, pin #5 is the plate of diode #1, pin #6 is missing, pin #7 is the other end of the heater, and pin #8 is the cathode of diode #1.

The octal socket is a receptacle for octal-base tubes with terminals to which leads may be soldered to make contact with the pins of the tube. The numbering of these terminals corresponds to that of the tube pins.

DIODE DETECTOR RECEIVER

16

CONSTRUCTION

Examine the photographs of the project to plan your layout of components, keeping in mind that leads should be as short as possible. Sketch your proposed layout on a sheet of paper and show it to your instructor for his approval.

Center-punch all holes and drill them. The hole beneath the antenna coil and the hole for the tube socket may be cut with a socket punch. Mount all components on the chassis.

Make a copy of the circuit diagram on a separate sheet of paper and make the connections between components as indicated by the circuit diagram, marking each connection with a colored pencil as you make it. (Be sure you make the proper connections to the antenna coil and tube socket.)

TESTING AND OPERATION

Check your wiring to see that all connections have been made properly. Also check each soldered joint. Then show your project to your instructor for his approval.

To operate your set, connect the antenna, ground, and headphones. Insert the tube in its socket and plug the line-cord resistor into the power outlet. Allow a few minutes for the tube to heat up. Mount the phones on your head and rotate the tuning knob slowly from one end of the dial to the other. Make a note of the position on the dial where each station you receive attains its maximum volume.

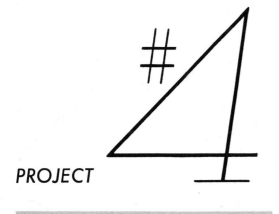

THE REGENERATIVE RECEIVER

REFERENCES

Elements of Radio, 3rd Edition. Pages 108-136.

Radio Servicing, 2nd Edition. Pages 101-104, 226-229.

GENERAL INFORMATION

In this project a triode is used as a detector. Because of the amplifying action of the tube, this receiver is more sensitive and its output signal is louder than that produced by a receiver employing a crystal or diode detector. In addition, some of the energy in the plate circuit of the tube is fed back to the grid circuit for further amplification in the tube. This is called *regenerative feedback.*

As a result, the receiver becomes even more sensitive and a still louder signal is produced in the headphones. In fact, this feedback and amplification process may be continued until the receiver becomes a miniature transmitter, producing a loud whistle or squeal that is heard in the phones and that may be broadcast through the antenna to nearby receivers. For this reason a feedback, or regeneration, control (R_3) is incorporated in the receiver to limit the feedback to a point below that at which the receiver becomes a transmitter.

This receiver employs a high-gain triode (6SF5) as a grid-leak detector. The student will manufacture his own antenna coil by winding turns of wire on a bakelite form. In addition to the normal primary and secondary windings, this coil contains a tertiary, or *tickler,* winding (L_3) for feedback action. A potentiometer (R_3) across this tickler winding controls the amount of feedback.

In addition to the 6.3 volts required for the heater of the tube, this set needs a supply of B voltage for the plate. This B voltage (90 or more volts) may be obtained from B batteries or from one of the power supplies described in Projects 5 and 6. If the B batteries or power supplies are not available, it is advisable to construct Project 5 or 6 before starting this one.

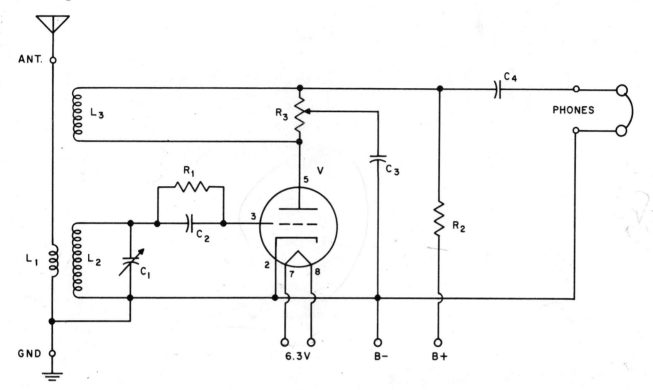

Circuit Diagram for Project No. 4

APPARATUS AND MATERIALS REQUIRED

C_1—Midget 0.000365-μf variable capacitor

C_2—0.0005-μf fixed capacitor (mica type)

C_3—0.00005-μf fixed capacitor (mica type)

C_4—0.01-μf fixed capacitor, 400v DCW (tubular-paper type)

$\left. \begin{array}{c} L_1 \\ L_2 \\ L_3 \end{array} \right\}$ Antenna coil wound with #30 enamel-covered copper wire on a 6-prong bakelite coil form 3″ long and 1½″ in diameter

R_1—2M-ohm, ½ watt, fixed resistor

R_2—500K-ohm, 1 watt, fixed resistor

R_3—50K-ohm potentiometer (regeneration control)

V—6SF5 high-gain triode

1 Pair headphones (2,000 ohms, or higher)

1 Octal socket (MIP type, or equivalent)

1 6-prong socket (MIP type, or equivalent)

1 Dial plate (0-100)

1 Large bar knob

1 Small knob

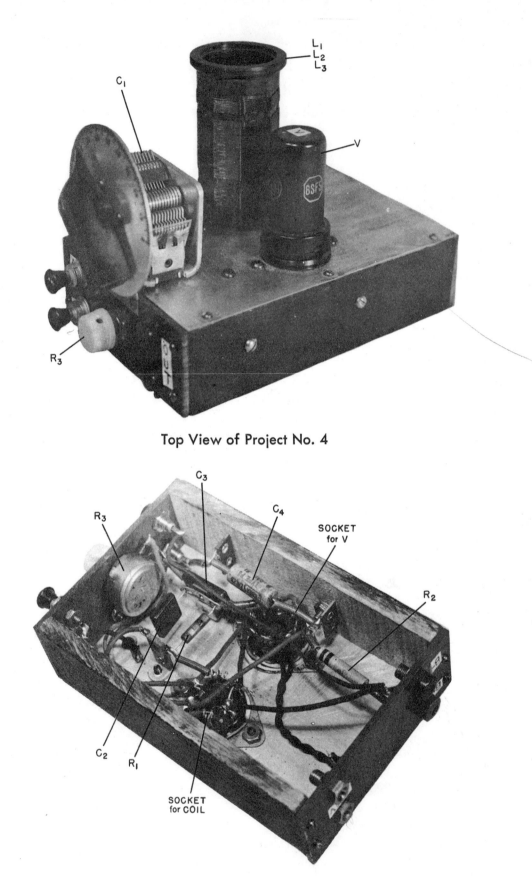

Top View of Project No. 4

Bottom View of Project No. 4

2 Binding posts (Antenna and Ground)
2 Tip jacks (for headphones)
4 Tip jacks (banana type), 1 red, 1 black, 2 plain
4 Tip plugs (banana type), 1 red, 3 black
Spool of #30 enamel-covered wire for coil windings
Chassis—6″ x 4″ x 1½″
Miscellaneous hardware (4 single tie lugs, woodscrews, machine bolts, nuts, washers).

COMPONENTS USED IN THIS PROJECT

Symbol

Explanation

Three-winding antenna coil

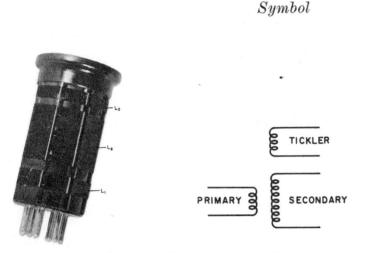

6-prong socket

Potentiometer

This coil contains six prongs which fit into the 6-prong socket and to which the terminals of the three windings connect. You will notice that two adjacent prongs are thicker than the others. If you hold the base of the coil form towards you with these two heavy prongs down, the left heavy prong is pin #1. The prong next to it in a clockwise direction is pin #2. Next to this is pin #3. And so on.

The 6-prong socket is a receptacle for the 6-prong coil form with terminals to which leads may be soldered to make contact with the windings of the coil. The numbering of these terminals corresponds to that of the coil form. You may notice a spot or pip on the top of the socket that is located between the contacts for the two heavy prongs.

When the shaft of the potentiometer is rotated, the resistance between the slider arm (indicated by the arrow in the symbol) and the end terminals is varied. The sliding-arm terminal is the center one of the potentiometer.

Potentiometers used in radio usually are of the composition or wire-wound types. Unless otherwise stated, potentiometers used in these projects are of the composition type.

6SF5 tube

The 6SF5 tube is a high-gain triode with an octal base. Pin #1 connects to the metal shell, pin #2 is the cathode, pin #3 is the grid, pin #4 is missing, pin #5 is the plate, pin #6 is missing, and pins #7 and #8 are the heater connections.

CONSTRUCTION

Examine the photographs of the project to plan your layout of components, keeping in mind that leads should be as short as possible, especially the grid and plate leads to the tube. Sketch your proposed layout on a sheet of paper and show it to your instructor for his approval.

Center-punch all holes and drill them. Mount all components on the chassis. Make a copy of the circuit diagram on a separate sheet of paper and, as you make the connections between components as indicated by the circuit diagram, mark each connnection with a colored pencil.

First wire in the heater leads. These two wires (from tip jacks to socket of the tube) should be twisted around each other to reduce a-c interference. Then make the other connections. As you make a connection to a terminal of the 6-prong socket, note the number of this terminal on your copy of the circuit diagram. This will help you make the proper connections between the windings and the base pins of your antenna coil.

About ⅛″ from the top of the coil form, drill a hole about ¹⁄₃₂″ in diameter. ¼″ below this hole, drill another. Drill another ⅛″ below this one, then another 1⅛″ below that, and another ⅛″ below that. Finally, drill another ⅜″ below the last one.

Clean the insulation off about an inch of the end of the #30 enamel-covered copper wire. To do so, fold a small piece of fine sandpaper so that the abrasive surfaces face each other. Place the end of the wire between these surfaces and, pressing lightly, draw the wire through. You should see the shiny copper surface as the enamel coating is rubbed off.

Note that the prongs of the coil form are hollow. Insert the cleaned wire through the first (top) hole in the form and thread the wire through one of the two prongs that are to terminate the tickler winding of the coil so that a portion of the wire protrudes from the end of the prong. Be sure that some of the cleaned wire is within the prong. With your soldering iron, melt some solder into the prong so that the wire is fastened to the prong. Remove the excess wire protruding out of the end of the prong and all excess solder on the outside of the prong so that it will fit into its socket.

Holding the coil form in one hand and rotating it, wind on 15 turns of wire. The wire is held in the other hand and a gentle tension is applied by the thumb. (Be sure that the spool is arranged so that the wire can come off without snagging.) The winding is to form a single layer with the turns next to each other. When the winding is completed, hold the turns in place with your thumb. Cut the wire about four inches beyond the last turn. Clean the free end of the wire so that a portion of the scraped wire will rest within the other prong of the tickler winding. Thread the wire through the second hole and through this prong. Solder and clean the prong as before.

Next comes the secondary winding, which consists of 100 turns wound in the same direction as the tickler winding. The wire is threaded through the third hole and through one of the two prongs that terminate the secondary winding. It is then soldered to that prong. After the winding is completed, the wire is threaded through the fourth hole and soldered to the other prong.

The primary winding, which consists of 20 turns wound in the same direction as the other two windings, is made in the same way. It terminates in the two remaining prongs. All windings should stay firmly in place. If they are loose, they may be held in place with a little collodion or scotch tape.

TESTING AND OPERATION

Check your wiring to see that all connections have been made properly. Also check each soldered joint. Then show your project to your instructor for his approval.

To operate your set, connect the antenna, ground, and headphones. Connect, too, the heater and B supply. (Be sure that all polarities are correct.) If a power supply is being used, insert its plug into the power outlet. Insert the tube and coil into their respective sockets. Turn on the switch of the power supply. Allow a few minutes for the tube to heat up.

Caution. Be careful when handling the power supply. While a shock from it may not be lethal, it is unpleasant.

Turn the regeneration control to its maximum (fully-clockwise) position. Rotate the tuning knob slowly from one end of the dial to the other, listening for a sharp whistle or squeal as a station is tuned in. If you get no whistle or squeal, turn the regeneration control fully counterclockwise and repeat. If you now get the whistle, turn off and disconnect the power supply. Then transpose the leads to the two end terminals of the regeneration-control potentiometer. Reconnect the power supply and note that the whistles now come at the fully-clockwise position of the control, which is as it should be.

If you get no whistles or squeals at either end of the regeneration control, disconnect the power supply and transpose the leads going to the tickler coil terminals at the 6-prong socket. Reconnect the power supply and try again. You now should get a squeal at one end of the regeneration control. If it be at the fully-counterclockwise position, disconnect the power supply and transpose the leads to the two end terminals of the potentiometer. Reconnect the power supply.

To tune in your station, set the regeneration control to its fully-clockwise position. Slowly rotate the tuning knob until the squeal is heard. Now slowly turn the regeneration control counterclockwise to the point where the squeal stops and the station is heard clearly. The point just before the squeal is heard is the most sensitive one.

Repeat this process for each station, making a note of the position on the dial at which it is located. Note, too, that the signals are louder than those heard on the simple crystal or diode detector receiver.

#5

PROJECT

A-C
POWER SUPPLY #1

REFERENCES

Elements of Radio, 3rd Edition. Pages 156-177.

Radio Servicing, 2nd Edition. Pages 92-94, 105-108, 119-121, 194-198, 515-528.

GENERAL INFORMATION

This project employs a type 80 tube as a full-wave rectifier. The power transformer (T) has a step-down secondary winding to provide the 5 volts required by the filament of the rectifier tube. Another step-down secondary winding provides the 6.3 volts required by the heaters of the tubes operating from this power supply. A third secondary winding is a center-tapped step-up type to supply the high B voltage.

The filter circuit consists of two electrolytic capacitors (C_1 and C_2) in a single metal can and a filter choke coil (L). The resistor (R) across the B-voltage output is a "bleeder resistor" that helps keep this B voltage at a constant level.

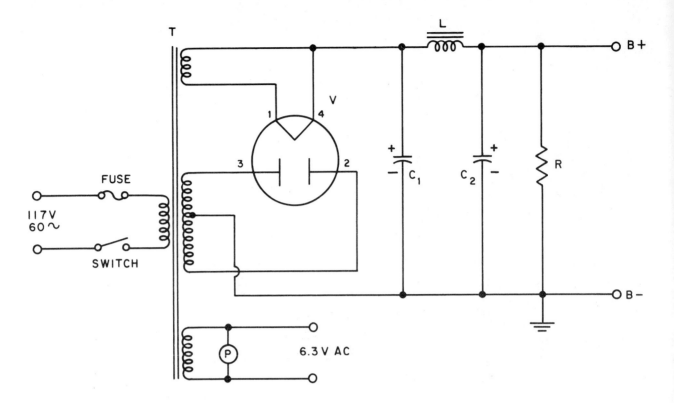

Circuit Diagram for Project No. 5

APPARATUS AND MATERIALS REQUIRED

C_1
C_2 } Dual 8-8-µf electrolytic capacitor, 450 volts DCW

L—Filter choke coil, 10 henrys at 120 milliamperes

R—25K-ohm, 25 watt, wire-wound fixed resistor

T—Power transformer. Primary. 117 volts, 60 cycles
     Secondary #1. 5 volts at 2 amperes
     Secondary #2. 6.3 volts at 2 amperes
     Secondary #3. 600 volts, center-tapped, at 0.12 amperes

V—Type 80 full-wave rectifier tube

1 4-prong socket (MIP type, or equivalent)

4 Tip jacks (banana type), 1 red, 1 black, 2 plain

4 Tip plugs (banana type), 1 red, 3 black

1 Fuse, type 8AG, 1 ampere

1 Fuse holder, for type 8AG fuse

1 Pilot lamp, #40, 6.3 volts at 0.15 ampere, miniature screw base

1 Pilot lamp holder and bezel, miniature screw base

1 Toggle switch, SPST

1 Male outlet plug

6 feet line cord (two leads)

Chassis 6″ x 7½″ x 1½″

Miscellaneous hardware (4 single tie lugs, woodscrews, machine bolts, nuts, washers).

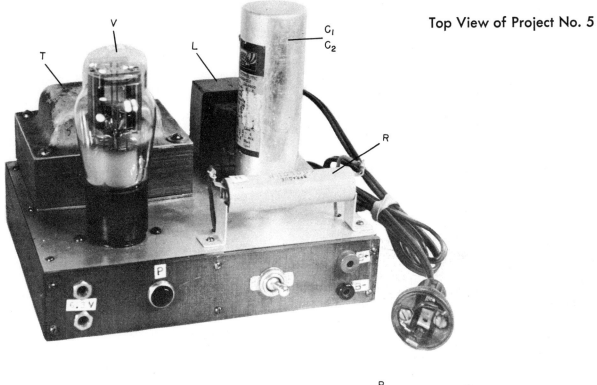

V

T

L

C₁
C₂

R

P

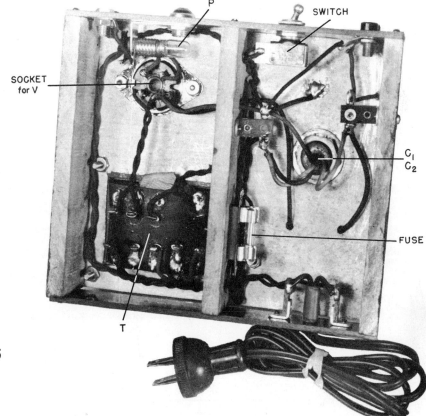

P

SWITCH

SOCKET
for V

C₁
C₂

FUSE

T

Bottom View of Project No. 5

A-C POWER SUPPLY #1

COMPONENTS USED IN THIS PROJECT

Symbol

Explanation

Electrolytic capacitor

The electrolytic capacitor is composed of two aluminum plates separated by a thin layer of aluminum oxide, which serves as the dielectric. The entire unit may be rolled into a cylinder to fit into a tubular aluminum can. Sometimes, the can itself may act as one plate.

Care must be taken not to exceed the capacitor's operating voltage, otherwise the dielectric may break down and the capacitor be ruined. Care, too, must be taken to connect this capacitor with correct polarity (as marked on the can). If incorrectly connected, the capacitor may be ruined.

In its symbol, the curved line indicates the negative terminal. Sometimes + and — signs are added to make this matter clearer. A single can may house more than one electrolytic capacitor.

Filter choke coil

The filter choke coil is an iron-cored inductance used in the filter circuit of the power supply. It is rated as to its inductance (in henrys) and its current-carrying capacity (in amperes).

This power transformer has three secondary windings. Secondary #1 furnishes 5 volts at 2 amperes for the filament of the 80

28

Symbol   *Explanation*

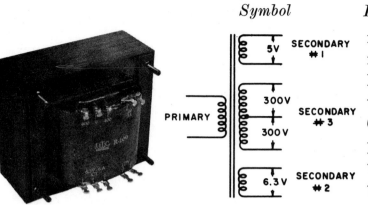

SECONDARY #1 5V

PRIMARY 300V SECONDARY #3 300V

6.3V SECONDARY #2

Power transformer

rectifier tube. Secondary #2 furnishes 6.3 volts at 2 amperes for the heaters of the tubes operating from this supply. Secondary #3 furnishes 600 volts, center-tapped, at 0.12 ampere for the B voltage required by the plates of tubes operating from this supply.

Type 80 tube

The 80 is a full-wave rectifier tube containing two plates and a filament in a single envelope. Its base has four pins. If you hold the base towards you, you will notice that two of the pins are heavier than the others. With the heavy pins down, the left heavy pin is #1. Next to it, in a clockwise direction, is pin #2. And so on.

Pin #1 connects to one end of the filament. Pin #2 is plate #2. Pin #3 is plate #1. Pin #4 is the other end of the filament. This filament requires 5 volts at 2 amperes.

4-prong socket

The 4-prong socket is a receptacle for the 80 tube. The numbering of the terminals of this socket corresponds to that of the tube. A dot or pip on the top of the socket is located between the contacts for the two heavy prongs.

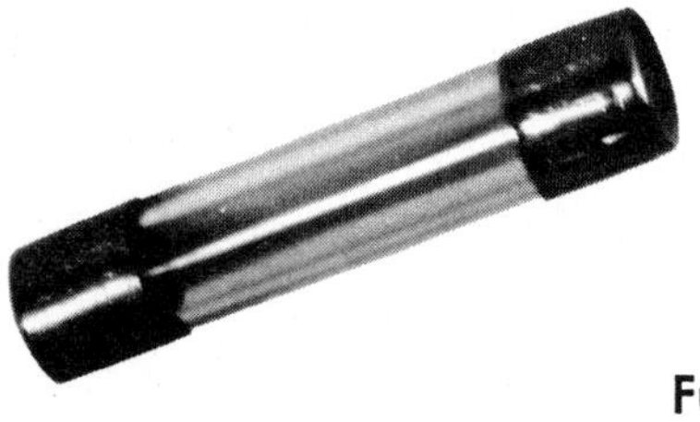

Fuse

Fuse holder

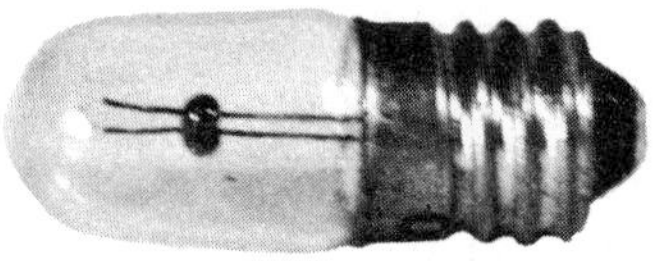

Pilot lamp

Pilot lamp holder

SPST toggle switch

Fuses are designed to melt when more than normal current flows through them, thus opening the circuit and protecting the other components. There are a number of different types of fuses. The one used in this project is a type 8AG. It consists of a thin wire of fusible metal in a glass tube. Metal caps make contact with the ends of the wire. Fuses are rated as to the maximum current they can carry without melting. The one used here is rated at 1 ampere.

The pilot lamp is a small lamp connected in the circuit so that it lights up when the current is on. It is rated by its required voltage and current. In this project the lamp used is a #40, operating at 6.3 volts at 0.15 ampere. Pilot lamps may have any of several types of base. The one used here has a miniature screw base. The pilot lamp holder should match the base of the lamp.

Circuits are opened or closed by moving the arm of the toggle switch to one side or the other. In this project a single circuit (the primary of the power transformer) is so controlled. The switch used here is a single-pole, single-throw (SPST) type.

CONSTRUCTION

Examine the photographs of the project to plan your layout of components, keeping in mind that leads should be as short as possible. Sketch your proposed layout on a sheet of paper and show it to your instructor for his approval.

A-C POWER SUPPLY #1

30

Center-punch all holes and drill them. The rectangular hole for the power transformer may be formed by the procedure that follows. First drill holes near each other around the inside of the space to be cut out. Next, using a cold chisel and hammer, cut away the material between these holes. Then file down the sides of the rectangular hole to its proper size. Be sure that the hole is large enough so that the transformer can fit on the chassis without any of its terminals shorting to the chassis and without any damage to the windings.

Mount all components on the chassis. Make a copy of the circuit diagram on a separate sheet of paper and, as you make the connections between components as indicated by the circuit diagram, mark each connection with a colored pencil.

First wire in the power transformer, making sure that the terminals are connected properly. Then wire in the other components. Be sure that the electrolytic capacitors are connected in their proper polarities.

TESTING AND OPERATION

Check your wiring to see that all connections have been made properly. Also check each soldered joint. Then show your project to your instructor for his approval.

The first test is to measure the output of the power supply. This output should consist of an alternating current, at about 6.3 volts, that supplies the heaters of the tubes connected to it and a direct current, at about 300 volts, which is the B supply for the plates and screens (if any) of these tubes.

The d-c B voltage is measured by means of a direct-current voltmeter connected between the B+ and B— tip jacks on the chassis of the power supply. The a-c heater voltage is measured by means of an alternating-current voltmeter connected between the heater tip jacks. (Refer to *Elements of Radio*, pages 376-383, 423, and 424.)

Of course, separate meters may be used. Or else, we may employ a *multimeter*, which consists of a number of measuring instruments all in one case and using the same meter movement. By means of a suitable switching arrangement we may select the type of instrument we want. For example, by setting the switches in a certain position we have a low-range a-c voltmeter for measuring the heater voltage. By varying the position of the switches we may change to a high-range d-c voltmeter for measuring the B voltage. (See *Radio Servicing*, pages 645-648.)

There are many types of suitable multimeters available. Since these instruments vary from each other in switching arrangements, ranges, etc., it is impossible to give a detailed testing procedure that would suit them all. Accordingly, a typical multimeter has been selected for demonstration. This is the Model 120, manufactured by Precision Apparatus Company, Inc., of New York City.

Caution. Be careful to avoid getting a shock when handling the high voltage furnished by this power supply. Although such a shock may not be fatal, it can be extremely unpleasant. Be sure that the switch is at its "off" position whenever you have to change any leads. Also, avoid touching any uninsulated portions of these leads when the switch is at its "on" position.

How the Precision Model 120 multimeter is connected to measure the B voltage of Project No. 5

The first test is to measure the B voltage produced by the power supply. If you examine the multimeter, you will notice two switches below the dial. One is an AC-DC switch that adapts the instrument to the type of current being measured. Since the B supply is a direct-current affair, this switch is turned to the "DC" position. The other switch determines the type of instrument (voltmeter, ammeter, ohmmeter, etc.) and its range. Since we expect to find a voltage of about 300 volts, this switch is turned to its "600 v" position.

Be sure that the plug of the power supply is *not* connected to the power outlet and that its switch is at the "off" position. Insert the rectifier tube into its socket, the fuse into its holder, and the pilot lamp into its holder. The banana-tip end of the black test lead is plugged into the jack on the panel of the multimeter that is marked "Common" and "—".

32

The other end of that lead is inserted into the B— jack (the black one) on the chassis of the power supply. The banana-tip end of the red test lead is plugged into the jack on the panel of the multimeter that is marked "+". The other end of that lead is inserted into the B+ jack (the red one) on the chassis of the power supply. *The correct polarity must be maintained, or the meter is likely to be ruined.* Ask your instructor to check your set-up before turning on the power.

Then insert the plug of the power supply into the power outlet and throw its switch to the "on" position. The pilot lamp should light up and the needle of the meter should swing to about the mid-scale position. You will take your reading on the 0-60 scale. However, since the full-scale range is 600 volts, multiply the reading by 10. For example, if the needle rests on the 30 mark of the 0-60 scale, the indicated voltage is 300 volts. Enter in your notebook the B voltage of the supply.

The next test is to measure the heater voltage produced by the power supply. Turn off the switch of the power supply and pull its plug from the outlet. Disconnect the black and red test leads from the B— and B+ jacks of the power supply.

Turn the AC-DC switch of the meter to the "AC" position. Since we expect the heater voltage to be about 6.3 volts, turn the range-selector switch to its "12 v" position. Insert the free end of the black test lead into one of the heater jacks (the plain ones) on the chassis of the power supply. Insert the free end of the red test lead into the other heater jack. (Since we are measuring an alternating current, the polarity of the leads does not matter.) Ask your instructor to check your set-up before turning on the power.

Then insert the plug of the power supply into the power outlet and throw its switch to the "on" position. Again, the pilot lamp should light up and the needle of the meter should swing to about the mid-scale position. This time the reading is taken directly on the 0-12 A.C. (red) scale. Enter in your notebook the heater voltage of the supply.

You will find both the B voltage and the heater voltage to be slightly higher than you had expected. This is because we are measuring them under no-load conditions. In actual operation, however, the load furnished by the tubes operating from this supply will drop these voltages somewhat. Show your instructor the voltage readings for his approval.

When you have measured the B and heater voltages of the power supply and found them to be satisfactory, the next test is to use this power supply with some device such as the Regenerative Receiver of Project No. 4. Turn off the switch of the power supply and remove its plug from the outlet. Connect leads between the heater jacks of the power supply and those of the receiver. Connect a lead between the B— jack (black) of the power supply and the B— jack (black) of the receiver. Connect a lead between the B+ jack (red) of the power supply and the B+ jack (red) of the receiver. Connect antenna, ground, and headphones to the receiver, turn on the power supply, and proceed to operate the receiver as indicated in Project No. 4.

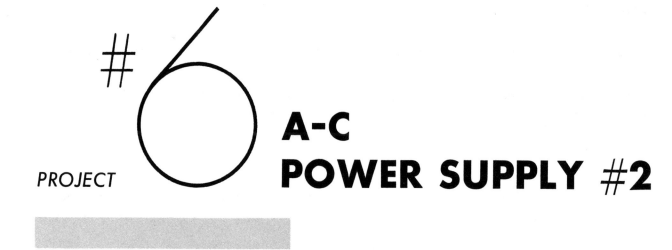

#6

PROJECT

A-C
POWER SUPPLY #2

REFERENCES

Elements of Radio, 3rd Edition. Pages 189 and 190.

Radio Servicing, 2nd Edition. Pages 107, 108, 173, 174, 191-194, 525, 544, 545.

GENERAL INFORMATION

This project does not employ a power transformer. Instead, the line voltage (117 volts) is rectified by a selenium rectifier in a half-wave circuit. Since there is no step-up action, the B-voltage output of this power supply is about equal to the line voltage.

The line voltage first is stepped down to 6.3 volts by the first filament transformer (T_1). This voltage is applied to the heaters of tubes operating from this power supply, and to the pilot lamp. The 6.3 volts are also applied to a second filament transformer (T_2) acting in reverse. That is, it is applied to the low-voltage winding of the transformer. This now acts as a step-up transformer, producing 117 volts across its high-voltage winding. This voltage, which equals the line voltage, is now applied to the rectifier and filter sections of the power supply.

The two transformers, in addition to supplying the heater and pilot lamp voltages, act to isolate the power line from the output of the power supply. Obviously, we could connect the line directly to the rectifier and filter sections of the power supply. But if we did, one end of the power line would be connected directly to the B— output of the supply. There would then be danger of a shock should we accidentally ground the B— post, or any device connected to it.

Note that the filter choke coil has been replaced by a resistor. This resistor acts to smooth out the ripples in the B voltage somewhat as the filter choke coil does. However, its d-c resistance is higher than that of the filter choke coil, and so the voltage drop across the resistor (for any given current flow) is greater than that produced across the filter choke coil. Since we have very little voltage to spare, because of the lack of step-up action, this type of power supply should be used only with devices drawing little B current. Also, since the smoothing action of the resistor is less than that of the filter choke coil, larger filter capacitors generally are used to compensate for this lack. Note, however, that the d-c working voltages of these filter capacitors are lower (150 volts, DCW).

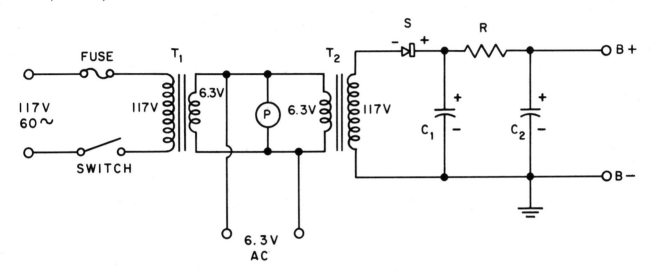

Circuit Diagram for Project No. 6

APPARATUS AND MATERIALS REQUIRED

$\begin{rcases} C_1 \\ C_2 \end{rcases}$ Dual 50-50-μf electrolytic capacitor, 150 volts, DCW

R—1,000-ohm, 10 watt, wire-wound fixed resistor

S—Selenium half-wave rectifier, 150 milliamperes

$\begin{rcases} T_1 \\ T_2 \end{rcases}$ Filament transformers. Primary. 117 volts, 60 cycles
            Secondary. 6.3 volts at 1 ampere

4 Tip jacks (banana type), 1 red, 1 black, 2 plain

4 Tip plugs (banana type), 1 red, 3 black

1 Fuse, type 8AG, 1 ampere

1 Fuse holder, for type 8AG fuse

1 Pilot lamp, #40, 6.3 volts at 0.15 ampere, miniature screw base

1 Pilot lamp holder and bezel, miniature screw base

1 Toggle switch, SPST

1 Male outlet plug

6 feet line cord (two leads)

Chassis 6" x 6" x 1½"

Miscellaneous hardware (2 single tie lugs, 1 double tie lug, 2 brackets for selenium rectifier, woodscrews, machine bolts, nuts, washers).

Top View of Project No. 6

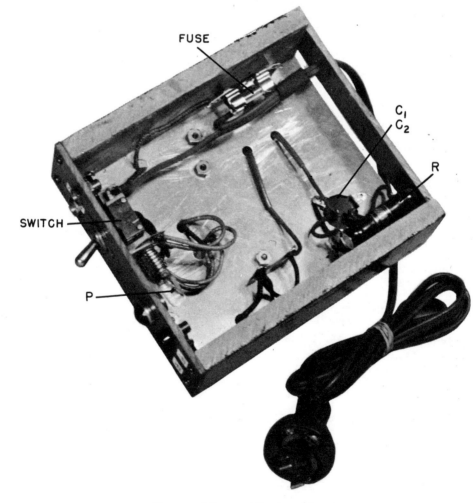

Bottom View of Project No. 6

COMPONENTS USED IN THIS PROJECT

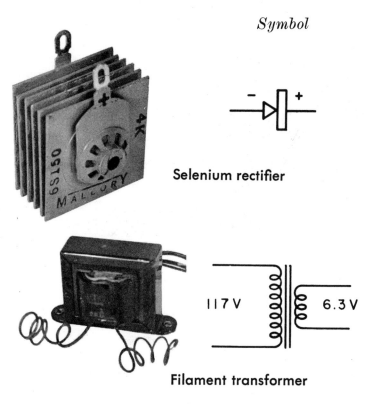

Symbol

Selenium rectifier

Filament transformer

117 V   6.3 V

Explanation

The selenium rectifier is a half-wave type, designed to operate from the line voltage (117 volts). Selenium rectifiers are rated by their current-carrying abilities, in this project 0.15 ampere. In the symbol, the bar connects to the B+ post

This transformer contains a primary winding (117 v) and a single step-down secondary winding (6.3 v) on an iron core.

CONSTRUCTION

Examine the photographs of the project to plan your layout of components, keeping in mind that leads should be as short as possible. Sketch your proposed layout on a sheet of paper and show it to your instructor for his approval.

Center-punch all holes and drill them. Mount all components on the chassis. Make a copy of the circuit diagram on a separate sheet of paper and, as you make the connections between components as indicated by the circuit diagram, mark each connection with a colored pencil. Be sure that you connect the selenium rectifier and the electrolytic capacitors in their proper polarities.

TESTING AND OPERATION

Check your wiring to see that all connections have been made properly. Also check each soldered joint. Then show your project to your instructor for his approval.

The testing and operating procedure for this power supply is identical with that described in Project No. 5, except that, since there is no step-up action here, the B voltage should be about equal to the line voltage (about 120 volts).

Measure the B and heater voltages under no-load conditions. Then connect this power supply to the Regenerative Receiver of Project No. 4 in place of the power supply of Project No. 5, and operate the receiver. Be sure to observe all the precautions indicated in Project No. 5.

A-C POWER SUPPLY #2

PROJECT 7

AUDIO-FREQUENCY AMPLIFIER

REFERENCES

Elements of Radio, 3rd Edition. Pages 137-155, 192-199, 261-265, 279-282, 583-605.

Radio Servicing, 2nd Edition. Pages 107, 112-117, 137-146, 156-159, 242-286, 299-306.

GENERAL INFORMATION

This project is a two-stage, resistance-coupled, audio-frequency amplifier. The input signal is fed through a potentiometer (R_1) which acts as a volume control. From there the signal passes to the grid of a high-gain triode (V_1) for amplification. The output of the triode is resistance-coupled to the control grid of a beam power tube (V_2) for further amplification. The output of the beam power tube is coupled to a permanent-magnet dynamic loudspeaker by means of an output transformer (T).

Note the inverse-feedback loop (R_7 and C_4) from the plate of V_2 to the cathode of V_1. The purpose of this feedback is to reduce distortion.

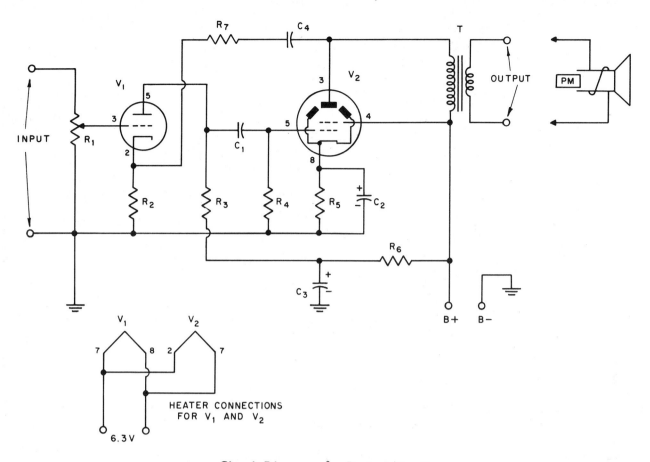

Circuit Diagram for Project No. 7

APPARATUS AND MATERIALS REQUIRED

C_1—0.01-μf fixed capacitor, 600v DCW (tubular-paper type)
C_2—25-μf electrolytic capacitor, 25v DCW
C_3—8-μf electrolytic capacitor, 450v DCW
C_4—0.01-μf fixed capacitor, 400v DCW (tubular-paper type)
R_1—500K-ohm potentiometer (volume control)
R_2—2.2K-ohm, ½ watt, fixed resistor
R_3—270K-ohm, 1 watt, fixed resistor
R_4—500K-ohm, ½ watt, fixed resistor
R_5—270-ohm, ½ watt, fixed resistor
R_6—100K-ohm, 1 watt, fixed resistor
R_7—100K-ohm, ½ watt, fixed resistor
T—Output transformer, 6V6-GT tube to 4-ohm voice coil
V_1—6SF5 high-gain triode
V_2—6V6-GT beam power tube
1 Loudspeaker, permanent-magnet dynamic type, mounted in wall baffle. Diameter 6″, voice
   coil 4 ohms, 3½ watts
2 Octal sockets (MIP type or equivalent)
1 Volume-control plate

AUDIO-FREQUENCY AMPLIFIER

1 Small knob for volume control
8 Tip jacks (banana type), 3 red, 3 black, 2 plain
8 Tip plugs (banana type), 3 red, 5 black
Chassis 6" x 5¼" x 1½"
Miscellaneous hardware (2 single tie lugs, woodscrews, machine bolts, nuts, washers).

Top View of Project No. 7

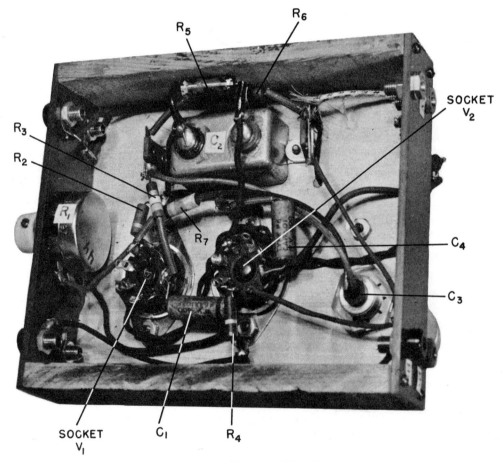

Bottom View of Project No. 7

COMPONENTS USED IN THIS PROJECT

Symbol   *Explanation*

Output transformer

The output transformer used here is of the universal type suitable for coupling any of a number of different types of power tubes to a loudspeaker whose voice coil has a definite resistance (in this case about 4 ohms). If you choose the proper primary and secondary connections, a proper match between the output stage and loudspeaker is assured.

In this project, the green lead of the primary winding goes to the plate of the 6V6-GT tube, and the white lead with the red tracer goes to the B+. The brown lead is not used, and its end is taped to prevent a short circuit.

The secondary winding has six taps. Taps Nos. 3 and 6 are connected to the voice coil of the loudspeaker.

Output transformers are rated as to the type of output tubes with which they are used, the circuit of the output stage (whether single-ended or push-pull), and the resistance of the voice coil of the loudspeaker connected to that stage. They are also rated as to how much power they can safely handle (in this case, about 4 watts).

AUDIO-FREQUENCY AMPLIFIER

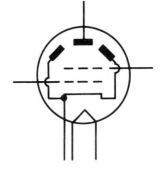

6V6-GT tube

The 6V6-GT tube is a beam power tube. Pin #1 is not used. Pin #2 is one end of the heater. Pin #3 is the plate. Pin #4 is the screen grid. Pin #5 is the control grid. Pin #6 is missing. Pin #7 is the other end of the heater. Pin #8 is the cathode. The beam-forming plates are internally connected to the cathode.

PM dynamic loudspeaker in wall baffle

The permanent-magnet dynamic loudspeaker is rated as to its size (in this project 6″ in diameter), the resistance of its voice coil (4 ohms), and the power it can safely handle (3½ watts).

Unless the speaker is mounted on a baffle, it will sound tinny. In this project a wall baffle is employed.

CONSTRUCTION

Examine the photographs of the project to plan your layout of components, keeping in mind that leads (especially plate and grid leads) should be as short as possible. Sketch your proposed layout on a sheet of paper and show it to your instructor for his approval.

Center-punch all holes and drill them. Mount all components on the chassis. Make a copy of the circuit diagram on a separate sheet of paper and, as you make the connections between components as indicated by the circuit diagram, mark each connection with a colored pencil. Be sure to connect correctly the tube sockets and output transformer. Also, be sure to connect the electrolytic capacitors in their proper polarities. The two voice-coil terminals of the loudspeaker are connected to 12-inch leads, each terminating in a banana-type tip plug.

AUDIO-FREQUENCY AMPLIFIER

TESTING AND OPERATION

Check your wiring to see that all connections have been made properly. Also check each soldered joint. Then show your project to your instructor for his approval.

The first test is to use this project to amplify a signal received by the Crystal Detector Receiver (Project No. 2). Use the A-C Power Supply No. 1 (Project No. 5) to power the amplifier. Making sure that the switch of the power supply is in its "off" position and that its plug is disconnected from the power outlet, run leads between the B+ and B— jacks of the power supply and those of the amplifier. (Be sure to observe the proper polarities.) Also run leads between the heater jacks of the power supply and those of the amplifier. Plug the loudspeaker into the output jacks of the amplifier. Insert the tubes into their proper sockets.

Set up and operate the Crystal Detector Receiver (as indicated in Project No. 2) to receive a fairly strong signal on the headphones. (If the signal is too weak it may not be able to operate the amplifier.) Leave the dial setting of the receiver in that position. Remove the headphones from the output jacks of the receiver. Place the amplifier next to the receiver and, using the shortest leads, connect the red output jack of the receiver to the red input jack of the amplifier. Also connect the black output jack of the receiver to the black input jack of the amplifier.

Insert the plug of the power supply into the power outlet and set its switch to the "on" position. Turn the volume-control knob of the amplifier to its fully-counterclockwise (minimum) position. Allow the tubes a few minutes to heat up.

Slowly rotate the volume-control knob of the amplifier in a clockwise direction. (If a loud hum is heard, transpose the plugs at the input jacks of the amplifier.) You should hear the signal in the loudspeaker, and its volume should increase the further the knob is rotated. If the action of the volume control is reversed—that is, maximum volume appears at the fully-counterclockwise position and minimum volume at the fully-clockwise position—turn off and disconnect the power supply from the amplifier and transpose the leads to the two end terminals of the volume-control potentiometer (R_1).

The second test is to operate the amplifier with the Diode Detector Receiver (Project No. 3). The procedure is the same as for the Crystal Detector Receiver.

The third test is to operate the amplifier with the Regenerative Receiver (Project No. 4). The procedure is the same as for the other two tests, except that the A-C Power Supply No. 2 (Project No. 6) is employed to power the receiver.

If a crystal-pickup record player is available, it may be used with this amplifier to form an electrical phonograph. The output leads from the crystal pickup should be connected directly to the input jacks of the amplifier. If one side of the crystal pickup is grounded, that side should be connected to the black input jack of the amplifier.

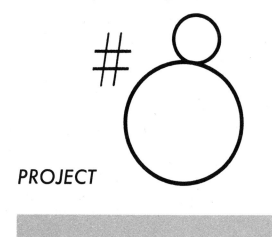

PROJECT **#8**

TUNED-RADIO-FREQUENCY TUNER

REFERENCES

Elements of Radio, 3rd Edition. Pages 200-219, 225-230, 270-278.

Radio Servicing, 2nd Edition. Pages 94-97, 108-112, 306-311, 392-397, 448.

GENERAL INFORMATION

This project is a tuner consisting of two stages of tuned-radio-frequency amplification, a diode detector stage, and a stage of audio-frequency amplification. The diode detector and audio-frequency stages employ the same multiunit tube V_3. Both manual- and automatic-volume control are included. Since the radio-frequency stages employ r-f pentodes (V_1 and V_2), neutralization of these stages is not required.

To complete the receiver, there must be added to this tuner a power supply (such as Project No. 5 or 6) and an audio-frequency amplifier (such as Project No. 7). Also required are antenna, ground, and loudspeaker.

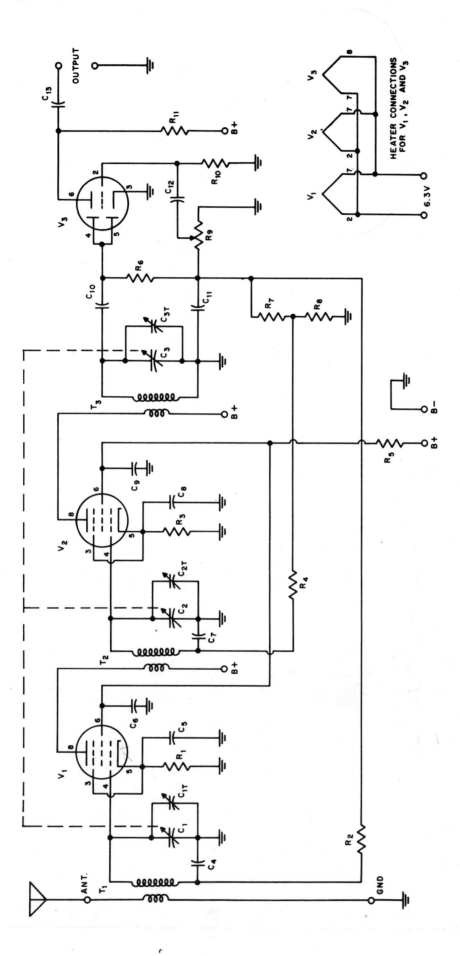

Circuit Diagram for Project No. 8

TUNED-RADIO-FREQUENCY TUNER

APPARATUS AND MATERIALS REQUIRED

$\left.\begin{array}{l} C_1 \\ C_2 \\ C_3 \end{array}\right\}$ Three-gang variable capacitor, 0.000365μf each section

$\left.\begin{array}{l} C_{1T} \\ C_{2T} \\ C_{3T} \end{array}\right\}$ Trimmer capacitors for C_1, C_2, and C_3, respectively

C_4—0.05-μf fixed capacitor, 200 v DCW (tubular-paper type)
C_5—0.1-μf fixed capacitor, 200 v DCW (tubular-paper type)
C_6—0.1-μf fixed capacitor, 400 v DCW (tubular-paper type)
C_7—0.05-μf fixed capacitor, 200 v DCW (tubular-paper type)
C_8—0.1-μf fixed capacitor, 200 v DCW (tubular-paper type)
C_9—0.1-μf fixed capacitor, 400 v DCW (tubular-paper type)
C_{10}—100-μμf fixed capacitor (mica type)
C_{11}—100-μμf fixed capacitor (mica type)
C_{12}—0.005-μf fixed capacitor, 600 v DCW (tubular-paper type)
C_{13}—0.05-μf fixed capacitor, 600 v DCW (tubular-paper type)
R_1—300-ohm, ½ watt, fixed resistor
R_2—2M-ohm, ½ watt, fixed resistor
R_3—300-ohm, ½ watt, fixed resistor
R_4—2M-ohm, ½ watt, fixed resistor
R_5—35K-ohm, 1 watt, fixed resistor
R_6—100K-ohm, ½ watt, fixed resistor
R_7—100K-ohm, ½ watt, fixed resistor
R_8—100K-ohm, ½ watt, fixed resistor
R_9—500K-ohm potentiometer (volume control)
R_{10}—10M-ohm, ½ watt, fixed resistor
R_{11}—250K-ohm, 1 watt, fixed resistor
T_1—Antenna coil (Meissner #14-1004, or equivalent)

$\left.\begin{array}{l} T_2 \\ T_3 \end{array}\right\}$ Radio-frequency transformers (Meissner #14-1005, or equivalent)

$\left.\begin{array}{l} V_1 \\ V_2 \end{array}\right\}$ 6SK7 super-control, r-f pentodes

V_3—6SQ7 duo-diode, high-gain triode
3 Octal sockets (MIP type or equivalent)
1 Dial plate (calibrated in kilocycles from 550 to 1750)
1 Dial knob and pointer
1 Volume-control plate
1 Small knob for volume control
2 Binding posts (Antenna and Ground)
2 Tip jacks (for headphones)
4 Tip jacks (banana type), 1 red, 1 black, 2 plain
4 Tip plugs (banana type), 1 red, 3 black
Chassis 6″ x 7½″ x 1½″
Miscellaneous hardware (2 single tie lugs, 3 double tie lugs, 1 triple tie lug, mounting brackets for variable capacitor, woodscrews, machine bolts, nuts, washers).

TUNED-RADIO-FREQUENCY TUNER

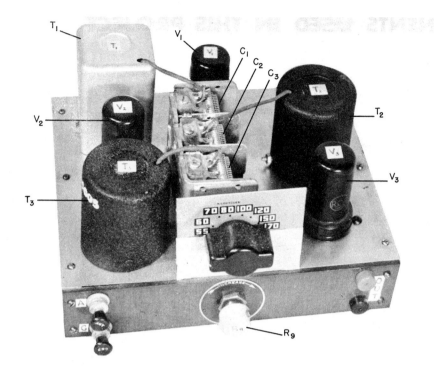

Top View of Project No. 8

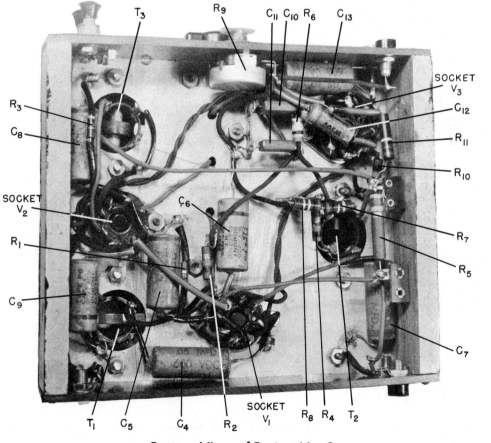

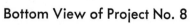

Bottom View of Project No. 8

TUNED-RADIO-FREQUENCY TUNER

47

COMPONENTS USED IN THIS PROJECT

Symbol	*Explanation*

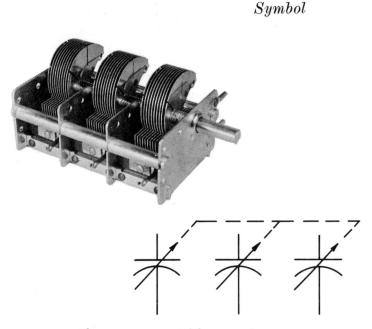

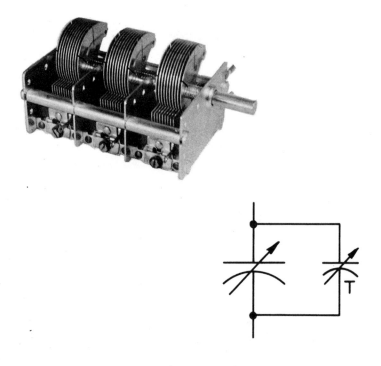

Two or more variable capacitors may be joined (*ganged*) together to be operated by a single dial. In this project a three-gang variable capacitor is employed.

In this project the two r-f amplifier stages and the detector stage are tuned simultaneously by means of a single dial. Therefore, all three stages must tune to exactly the same frequency for any setting of the dial.

Three-gang variable capacitor

Since there will always be some discrepancies between these stages, the variable capacitor that tunes each stage must be made adjustable (by some small amount) to compensate for these discrepancies. This is accomplished by connecting a small, semi-variable capacitor, called a *trimmer,* in parallel with each of the tuning variable capacitors. Adjustment of these trimmers will produce the proper compensation for the discrepancies between stages.

Generally, the trimmer capacitor consists of plates of phosphor bronze and sheet mica (the dielectric). These plates are arranged like the leaves of a book, and can be moved closer together or further apart by a screw adjustment, thereby varying the capacitance. Since the trimmer capacitor is in

Variable capacitor with trimmer

parallel with the tuning capacitor, the over-all capacitance is thus varied in small degree.

The trimmer capacitor may be a separate unit, but usually it is built right into the side of the variable tuning capacitor. There is a trimmer for each section of the variable tuning capacitor. In the circuit diagram, the trimmer capacitor is identified by the letter T appearing in its symbol.

The radio-frequency transformer (T_2 and T_3) is designed to cover the entire broadcast band (from 545 to 1580 kc) when its secondary is tuned with an 0.000365-µf variable capacitor.

The 6SK7 tube is a supercontrol, r-f pentode. Pin #1 connects to the metal shell. Pin #2 is one end of the heater. Pin #3 is the suppressor grid. Pin #4 is the control grid. Pin #5 is the cathode. Pin #6 is the screen grid. Pin #7 is the other end of the heater. Pin #8 is the plate.

The 6SQ7 tube consists of two diodes and a high-gain triode in a single envelope. Pin #1 connects to the shell. Pin #2 is the triode grid. Pin #3 is the common cathode. Pin #4 is the plate of diode No. 2. Pin #5 is the plate of diode No. 1. Pin #6 is the triode plate. Pins #7 and #8 are the ends of the heater. In this project the plates of both diodes are joined and, with the common cathode, form a single diode.

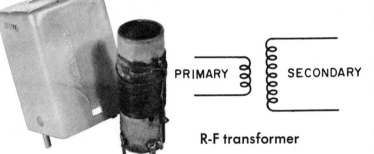

R-F transformer

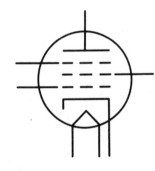

6SK7 tube

6SQ7 tube

TUNED-RADIO-FREQUENCY TUNER

49

CONSTRUCTION

Examine the photographs of the project to plan your layout of components, keeping in mind that leads (especially plate and grid leads) should be as short as possible. Note that the three-gang variable tuning capacitor is mounted on its side. This is done so that the screws of the trimmer capacitors face upwards and so are available for adjustment. Because of this, the grid leads of the antenna coil and r-f transformers are brought out through a hole in the top of each shield can to connect to the variable tuning capacitor. Sketch your proposed layout on a sheet of paper and show it to your instructor for his approval.

Center-punch all holes and drill them. Mount all components on the chassis. Make a copy of the circuit diagram on a separate sheet of paper and, as you make the connections between components as indicated by the circuit diagram, mark each connection with a colored pencil. Be sure to connect the tube sockets and the various coils correctly.

TESTING AND OPERATION

Check your wiring to see that all connections have been made properly. Also check each soldered joint. Then show your project to your instructor for his approval.

In this tuner there are three tuned circuits that must tune, or resonate, at the same frequency at the same time. That is to say, if the tuned circuit consisting of T_1 and C_1 is tuned to 1400 kilocycles, for example, the tuned circuit consisting of T_2 and C_2 also must be tuned to 1400 kilocycles. And so must the tuned circuit consisting of T_3 and C_3. These three tuned circuits are controlled by means of the three-gang variable capacitor operating from a single tuning dial.

Since it is impossible to avoid slight discrepancies between the various tuned circuits, the small trimmer capacitors in parallel with each of the larger tuning capacitors are provided to compensate for these discrepancies. Alignment consists of so adjusting each of the trimmer capacitors that all three tuned circuits resonate simultaneously at the same frequency.

The procedure consists of feeding a radio signal of known frequency to the receiver, setting the dial of the receiver to indicate that frequency, and then adjusting, one at a time, the three trimmer capacitors to obtain the maximum reception of that signal.

(Sometimes, the three-gang tuning capacitor is not equipped with trimmers. Instead, the end rotor plates of each section are slotted and alignment is achieved by slightly bending these slotted plates back or forth to vary the over-all capacitance of each section. The result is the same as that accomplished by the trimmers. In some cases both trimmers and slotted plates are employed. It is usual, then, to use the trimmers for alignment at the high-frequency end of the tuning range and the slotted plates for alignment at the low-frequency end.)

The radio signal, of course, may be any strong broadcast signal. It is more convenient, however, to use a signal from a signal generator. (See *Radio Servicing,* pages 649-659.) There are many types of suitable signal generators available. Since these instruments vary from each other in switching arrangements, ranges, etc., it is impossible to give a detailed operating procedure that would suit them all. Accordingly, a typical signal generator has been selected for demonstration. This is the Series E-200-C, manufactured by Precision Apparatus Company, Inc., of New York City.

This instrument is capable of generating a signal of any frequency between 88 kilocycles and 240 megacycles. This signal may be unmodulated, modulated by means of a 400-cycle internal audio oscillator, or else modulated by means of an external source. In addition, we may obtain a 400-cycle, sine-wave audio signal.

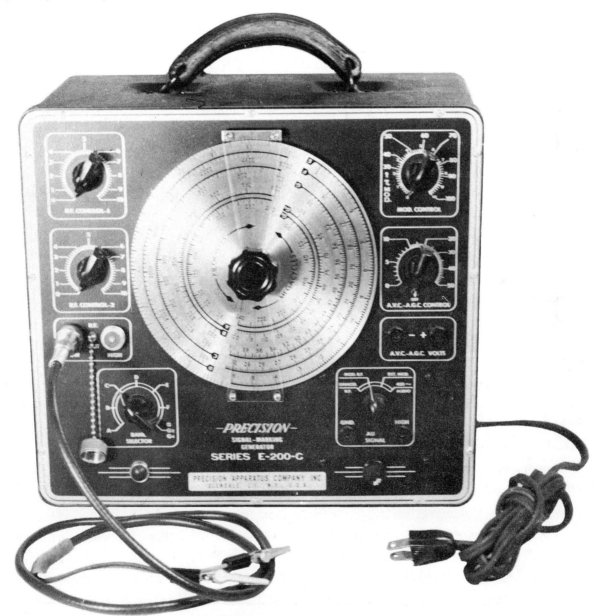

Precision Series E-200-C signal generator

The switch in the lower right-hand corner selects the signal to be put out by the generator. If an r-f signal (either modulated or unmodulated) is desired, output is obtained from one of the two coaxial cable connectors at the left center of the panel. The operator can obtain low or high output as desired by selecting the proper connector.

The frequency of the signal is determined by the setting of the large center dial and the band selected by the Band Selector switch. The volume of the signal is determined by R.F. Control-1 (which is the coarse adjustment) and R.F. Control-2 (which is the fine adjustment).

If a modulated r-f signal is desired, the Modulation Control determines the percentage of modulation. If the 400-cycle audio signal is desired, the signal-selector switch is set to "400 ~ Audio" and the signal is obtained from the two jacks marked "Gnd" and "High".

The first step is to set up the Audio-Frequency Amplifier as indicated in Project No. 7. Use the A-C Power Supply No. 1 (Project No. 5) to power the amplifier. Connect the output of the Tuned-Radio-Frequency Tuner to the input of the amplifier, using short leads and observing correct polarities. Use the A-C Power Supply No. 2 (Project No. 6) to power the tuner.

Connect the coaxial cable of the signal generator to the cable connector marked "High". The other end of this cable terminates in two alligator clips. Connect the black clip to the ground post of the tuner and run a lead from that post to some good ground connection. Connect the red clip to the antenna post of the tuner through an 0.00025-μf mica capacitor.

Set the signal-selector switch to "Mod.R.F.", the Modulation Control to zero, the Band Selector to "C", R.F. Control-1 to zero, and R.F. Control-2 to zero. Insert the plug of the generator into the power outlet and set the A.V.C.—A.G.C. Control to zero. This turns on the generator.

Next, insert the plugs of the power supplies into their respective power outlets. Turn on these power supplies and allow generator, power supplies, tuner, and amplifier to warm up for about ten minutes.

Turn the volume control (R_9) to its maximum (fully-clockwise) position. (If, during this procedure you find that this volume control is reversed, turn off the power supplies and transpose the leads to the two outside terminals of the volume-control potentiometer.) Set the dial of the tuner at 1400 kilocycles. Turn the volume control of the amplifier to maximum.

Turn the dial of the signal generator until the red line coincides with 1400 kilocycles on Band C. Set the Modulation Control at 30%. Set R.F. Control-1 at 1 and turn up R.F. Control-2 until a 400-cycle whistle is heard coming from the loudspeaker. Should R.F. Control-2 reach 10 and no whistle be heard, increase the setting of R.F. Control-1. If there still is no whistle, increase the setting of the Modulation Control.

When the whistle is heard, adjust the R.F. Controls of the generator to give a faint, but distinct signal. Now adjust trimmer capacitor C_{3T} of the tuner for maximum volume. Reduce the volume of the whistle again by means of the R.F. Controls. Adjust trimmer capacitor C_{2T} for maximum volume. Repeat for trimmer capacitor C_{1T}. This completes the high-frequency alignment.

Turn the tuner dial to 600 kilocycles. Turn the signal generator dial until the red line coincides with 600 kilocycles on Band C. Repeat the high-frequency alignment, but this time, instead of adjusting the trimmers, bend the slotted end plates of capacitors C_3, C_2, and C_1 (in that order) slightly back or forth for maximum signal strength. (Be sure not to permit these end plates to touch the stator plates.) This completes the low-frequency alignment. Now repeat the high-frequency alignment.

Sometimes, if the tuner is very much out of alignment, it may not be possible to obtain the 400-cycle whistle when the signal from the generator is fed to the antenna post of the tuner. In that case, feed the signal (through the 0.00025-μf capacitor) to the control grid (pin #4) of V_2 and align only the detector tuning circuit (C_{3T} and C_3). Then feed the signal to the control grid (pin #4) of V_1 and align the tuning circuit of the second r-f stage (C_{2T} and C_2). Finally, feed the signal to the antenna post and align the entire tuner.

(If a signal generator is not available, a strong broadcast signal may be used instead. For this purpose, a good antenna and ground are required. This antenna may be connected to the antenna post of the receiver or, if need be, to the control grid of V_1 or V_2. The alignment procedure is the same as that previously described.)

The alignment procedure completed, disconnect the signal generator and, in its place, connect an antenna and ground. Make a note of the position on the dial of the tuner at which each station is received.

#9

PROJECT

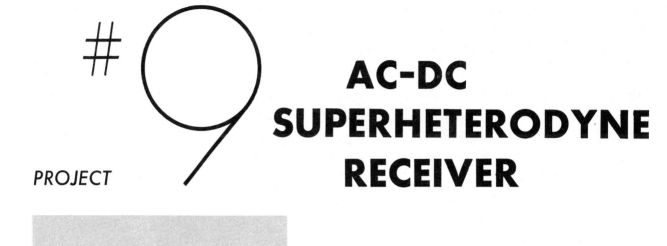

AC-DC SUPERHETERODYNE RECEIVER

REFERENCES

Elements of Radio, 3rd Edition. Pages 240-258, 282-286, 307-311, 621-632.

Radio Servicing, 2nd Edition. Pages 111, 112, 312-316, 333-348, 448-467, 544-552.

GENERAL INFORMATION

This project is a superheterodyne receiver consisting of a converter stage, a stage of intermediate-frequency amplification, a stage consisting of diode detector and audio-frequency amplifier, an audio-frequency output stage, and an AC-DC power supply using a half-wave rectifier (V_5). The voltage drop across the heaters of all the tubes in series is equal to approximately 120 volts and, hence, when these series-connected heaters are placed across the line, no voltage-dropping resistor is required. The pilot lamp (P) is connected across a portion of the heater of the rectifier tube.

Note that the B— line connects to one side of the power line. If the B— line were also to be connected directly to the chassis, the chassis, and all components mounted on it, might be "hot." That is, when the plug of the receiver was inserted into the power outlet, its polarity might be such as to place the chassis 117 volts above ground. Should the student be grounded as he touched the chassis, he would receive a shock.

Accordingly, all the B— connections are made to the B— line, which is insulated from the chassis. The decoupling filter, consisting of R_9 and C_{12}, effectively connects the chassis to the B— line (as far as the signal is concerned) and yet keeps the line voltage off the chassis, thus eliminating the possibility of a shock.

AC-DC SUPERHETERODYNE RECEIVER

54

Capacitor C_1, which tunes the loop antenna (L_1), and capacitor C_2, which tunes the local oscillator coil (L_2) form a two-gang unit. To enable the local oscillator to track with the incoming signal, capacitor C_2 has smaller and fewer rotor plates than does C_1. In this way the frequency of the local oscillator is always 456 kilocycles (the intermediate frequency) above that of the incoming signal. The output of the oscillator is fed to the converter tube (V_1) by means of capacitive coupling between the turns of L_2 and L_3.

Note that the stators of C_1 and C_2 are not connected directly to the chassis. Accordingly, the two-gang variable capacitor is mounted on insulators. In the case of electrolytic capacitors C_{10} and C_{11} the can that houses this dual unit usually is the common negative terminal. This negative terminal, too, does not connect directly to the chassis and must be insulated from it.

Automatic-volume control is furnished by means of the AVC network consisting of R_2, C_4, and C_6. Potentiometer R_3 is the manual-volume control. The on-off switch (S) is mounted on this potentiometer and the first few degrees of rotation in a clockwise direction turns the set on. To turn the set off, the volume control must be turned fully counterclockwise.

APPARATUS AND MATERIALS REQUIRED

C_1
C_2 } Two-gang variable capacitor. $C_1 = 0.000365\mu f$ $C_2 = 0.000108\mu f$

C_{1T}
C_{2T} } Trimmer capacitors for C_1 and C_2, respectively

C_3—0.02-μf fixed capacitor, 400 v DCW (ceramic type)

C_4—0.05-μf fixed capacitor, 400 v DCW (tubular-paper type)

C_5—0.005-μf fixed capacitor, 400 v DCW tubular-paper type)

C_6—330-$\mu\mu f$ fixed capacitor, 400 v DCW (ceramic type)

C_7—330-$\mu\mu f$ fixed capacitor, 400 v DCW (ceramic type)

C_8—0.01-μf fixed capacitor, 400 v DCW tubular-paper type)

C_9—0.02-μf fixed capacitor, 400 v DCW (ceramic type)

C_{10}
C_{11} } Dual 30-30-μf electrolytic capacitor, 150 v DCW

C_{12}—0.05-μf fixed capacitor, 400 v DCW (tubular-paper type)

C_{13}—0.05-μf fixed capacitor, 400 v DCW (tubular-paper type)

L_1—Loop antenna, to operate with 0.000365-μf variable capacitor

L_2 ⎱ Oscillator coil, to operate with 0.000108-μf variable capacitor
L_3 ⎰ Winding that capacitively couples oscillator to V_1 (Meissner #14-1073, or equivalent)

R_1—22K-ohm, ½ watt, fixed resistor

R_2—2.2M-ohm, ½ watt, fixed resistor

R_3—500K-ohm potentiometer (volume control) with SPST switch (S) mounted on rear

R_4—4.7M-ohm, ½ watt, fixed resistor

R_5—470K-ohm, ½ watt, fixed resistor

R_6—470K-ohm, ½ watt, fixed resistor

R_7—150-ohm, ½ watt, fixed resistor

R_8—2200-ohm, 1 watt, fixed resistor

R_9—470K-ohm, ½ watt, fixed resistor

AC-DC SUPERHETERODYNE RECEIVER

56

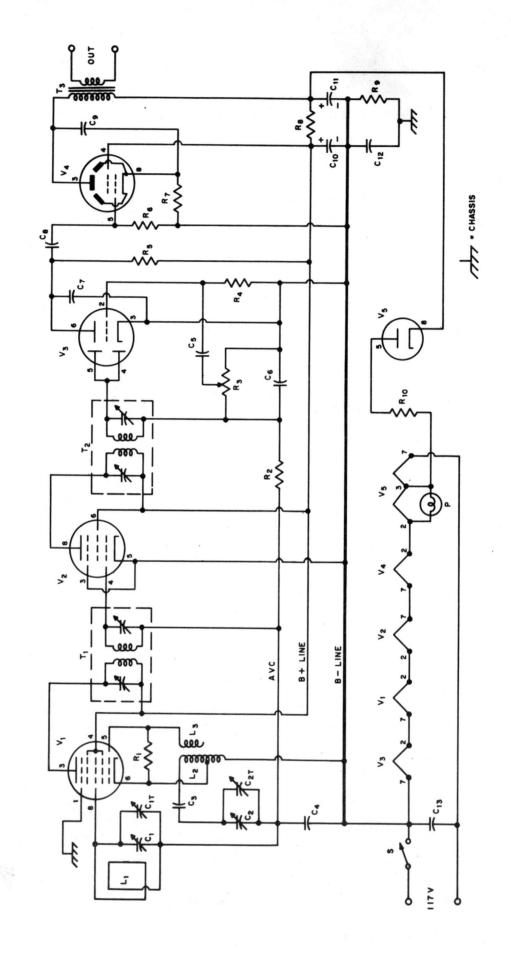

Circuit Diagram for Project No. 9

R$_{10}$—22-ohm, ½ watt, fixed resistor

S—Single-pole, single-throw switch mounted on rear of volume-control potentiometer (R$_3$)

T$_1$—First intermediate-frequency transformer. 456kc (Meissner # 16-6658, or equivalent)

T$_2$—Second intermediate-frequency transformer. 456kc (Meissner #16-6658, or equivalent)

T$_3$—Output transformer, 50L6-GT tube to 4-ohm voice coil

V$_1$—12SA7 pentagrid converter

V$_2$—12SK7 super-control, r-f pentode

V$_3$—12SQ7-GT duo-diode, high-gain triode

V$_4$—50L6-GT beam power amplifier

V$_5$—35Z5-GT half-wave rectifier

P—Pilot lamp, #40, 6.3 volts at 0.15 ampere, miniature screw base

1 Pilot lamp holder and bezel, miniature screw base

5 Octal sockets

1 Dial plate (calibrated in kilocycles from 550 to 1750)

1 Dial knob

1 Volume-control plate

1 Small knob for volume control

2 Tip jacks (banana type) 1 red, 1 black

2 Tip plugs (banana type) 1 red, 1 black

1 Loudspeaker, permanent-magnet dynamic type, mounted in wall baffle; diameter 6″, voice coil 4 ohms, 3½ watts

1 Male outlet plug

6 feet line cord (two leads)

Chassis 6″ x 7½″ x 1½″

Miscellaneous hardware (4 single tie lugs, 2 double tie lugs, brackets for loop antenna, insulators for variable capacitors and electrolytic capacitors, woodscrews, machine bolts, nuts, washers).

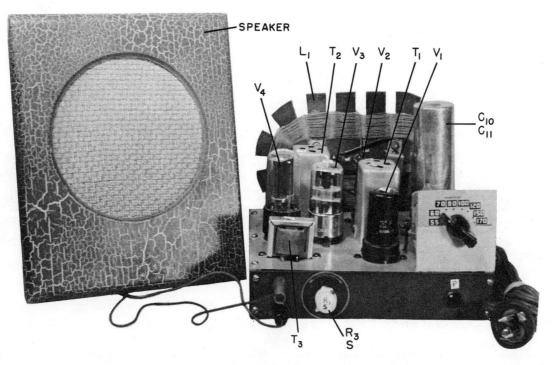

Top View of Project No. 9

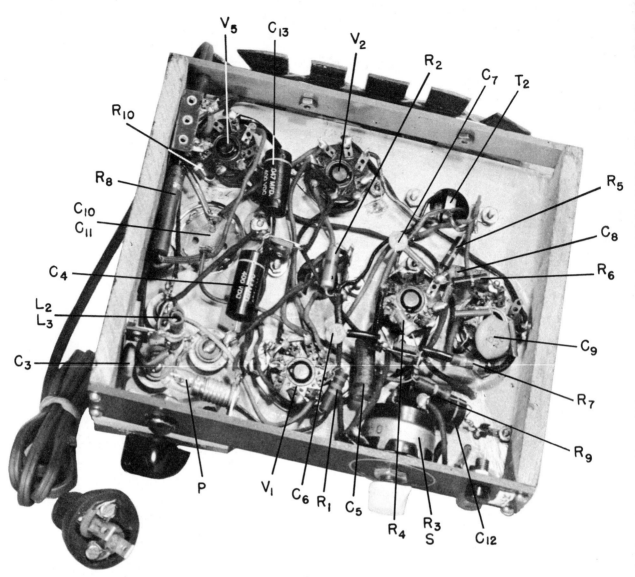

Bottom View of Project No. 9

COMPONENTS USED IN THIS PROJECT

Symbol

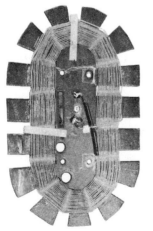

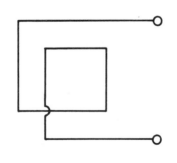

Loop antenna

Explanation

As its name implies, the loop antenna consists of turns, or loops, of wire wound on a form, usually made of cardboard. The result is a compact antenna that can be housed in the same cabinet as the radio.

The loop antenna is not as sensitive as an equivalent straight-wire antenna. However, this does not matter with a receiver as sensitive as the superheterodyne type.

58

The loop antenna is directional. That is, it will receive signals better when the broad, flat side of the loop is facing the source.

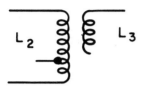

Oscillator coil

The oscillator coil (L_2) is tuned by the smaller of the ganged variable capacitors to generate an unmodulated signal that, at all times, is 456 kilocycles higher in frequency than the incoming signal. By heterodyne action, the oscillator signal and the incoming signal are mixed in V_1 to produce a beat signal at the intermediate frequency (456 kc).

Output from the oscillator coil is fed to V_1 by capacitive action between the windings of L_2 and those of L_3.

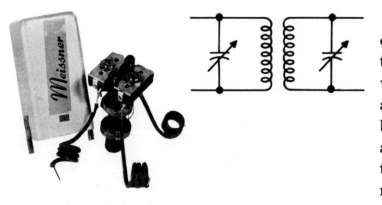

Intermediate-frequency transformer

There are a number of different types of intermediate-frequency transformers. In this project, the windings are air-cored. Primary and secondary are tuned separately by means of a trimmer capacitor across each winding. Windings and trimmers are contained in a common can which also acts as a shield.

In other types of transformers, the windings may have powdered-iron cores. Tuning may be accomplished by moving the cores in or out of the coils. Sometimes only one of the windings is tunable.

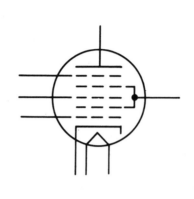

12SA7 tube

The 12SA7 tube is a pentagrid converter type. Pin #1 connects to the metal shell and grid #5. (The grids of the tube are numbered by calling the one closest to the cathode #1, the next one #2, and so on. Thus grid #5 is the fifth grid from the cathode, and the closest to the plate.) Pin #2 is one end of the heater. Pin #3 is the plate. Pin #4 connects to grids #2 and #4 (which are connected internally). Pin #5 is grid #1. Pin #6 is the cathode. Pin #7 is the other end of the heater. Pin #8 is grid #3.

The 12SK7 tube is a super-control, r-f pentode identical with the 6SK7 tube described in Project No. 8, except that the heater requires 12.6 volts at 0.15 ampere instead of the 6.3 volts at 0.3 ampere required for the 6SK7 tube. The pin connections for the two tubes are identical.

The 12SQ7-GT tube is identical with the 6SQ7 tube described in Project No. 8, except that it is a glass type instead of metal and that its heater requires 12.6 volts at 0.15 ampere instead of the 6.3 volts at 0.3 ampere required for the 6SQ7 tube. The pin connections for the two tubes, too, are identical, except that pin #1 of the metal type (6SQ7) connects to the metal shell, whereas pin #1 of the glass type (12SQ7-GT) connects to the base sleeve of the tube.

AC-DC SUPERHETERODYNE RECEIVER

60

Symbol   *Explanation*

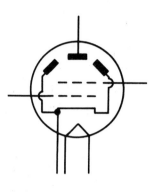

50L6-GT tube

The 50L6-GT tube is a beam power amplifier that is used in the audio output stage. Pin #1 is missing. Pin #2 is one end of the heater. Pin #3 is the plate. Pin #4 is the screen grid. Pin #5 is the control grid. Pin #6 is missing. Pin #7 is the other end of the heater. Pin #8 is the cathode.

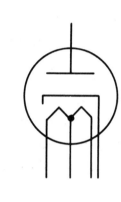

35Z5-GT tube

The 35Z5-GT tube is a half-wave rectifier. The panel lamp, which connects across pins #2 and #3 of the tube, should be of the 6.3-volt type, operating at 0.15 ampere (No. 40 or No. 47).

Pin #1 is unconnected. Pin #2 is one end of the heater. Pin #3 is the heater tap. Pin #4 is missing. Pin #5 is the plate. Pin #6 is missing. Pin #7 is the other end of the heater. Pin #8 is the cathode.

CONSTRUCTION

Examine the photographs of the project to plan your layout of components, keeping in mind that leads (especially plate and grid leads) should be as short as possible. Note that variable capacitors C_1 and C_2 and the metal can containing capacitors C_{10} and C_{11} (where the can is the common negative) are insulated from the metal chassis. Sketch your proposed layout on a sheet of paper and show it to your instructor for his approval.

Center-punch all holes and drill them. Mount all components on the chassis. Make a copy of the circuit diagram on a separate sheet of paper and, as you make the connections between components as indicated by the circuit diagram, mark each connection with a colored pencil.

Be sure to connect correctly the tube sockets and the various inductors. Also, be sure to connect pin #1 of V_1 and V_2 to the chassis. In this way the metal shells act as shields and help prevent the set from regenerating.

TESTING AND OPERATION

Check your wiring to see that all connections have been made properly. Also check each soldered joint. Then show your project to your instructor for his approval.

The alignment procedure consists of injecting suitable signals into various portions of the receiver and making the various adjustments to obtain maximum output. For this purpose we may use a signal generator such as the Precision Series E-200-C described in Project No. 8.

Maximum output may be determined by the loudness of the signal coming from the loudspeaker. A more satisfactory method, however, is to connect an output meter across the voice coil of the loudspeaker, making adjustments for maximum readings on the meter. The Precision Model 120 multimeter described in Project No. 5 may be used as such an output meter by plugging the test leads into the jacks marked "Common" and "Output", setting the AC-DC switch to "AC", and selecting a suitable range by means of the range-selecting switch. To obtain the proper range, set the switch at the highest range and then reduce it until a significant reading appears on the meter.

Insert the tubes and pilot lamp into their respective sockets and connect the loud-speaker to the output jacks. Turn the volume control fully counterclockwise. This is the "off" position for switch S. Insert the plug into the power outlet. Turn the volume control in a clockwise direction. At the very start you should hear a click which indicates that switch S has been thrown "on". The heaters of the tubes and the pilot lamp should light up.

Set up the multimeter as an output meter (as described above) and set the range-selector switch to 300 volts. Connect the test leads to the voice coil of the loudspeaker.

The first check is to see if the audio-frequency section of the receiver is operating properly. For this we want the 400-cycle audio signal from the signal generator. Set the signal-selector switch to "400~Audio". Insert a test lead into each of the two jacks (marked "Gnd." and "High") beneath that switch. Connect the test lead from the "Gnd." jack to the chassis of the receiver. Turn the A.V.C.-A.G.C. Control to zero. This turns on the signal generator. Allow about ten minutes for the generator to warm up and stabilize.

Touch the lead from the "High" jack to pin #5 of V_4. The 400-cycle whistle should be heard in the loudspeaker. (If no whistle is heard, try changing tube V_4.) Reduce the voltage range of the output meter (by means of the range-selecting switch) until a reading of several divisions on the scale is obtained. (In our use of an output meter, we are interested in relative values, rather than absolute values. In other words, we wish to know if the signal is increasing or decreasing rather than its value at any given time.)

Next turn the volume control to maximum volume (fully clockwise) and touch the lead to the terminal of the volume-control potentiometer (R_3) that connects to R_2 and C_6.

The signal should be louder and the reading on the output meter higher due to the amplifying action of the triode section of V_3. (Watch the meter carefully to see that the needle does not go off-scale. If necessary, choose a higher range.) If there is no increase in volume and reading, try changing tube V_3.

It may be, however, that the volume control is reversed. In that case, disconnect the receiver from the power outlet and transpose the two outside leads to potentiometer R_3.

The next step is to align the intermediate-frequency transformers T_1 and T_2. These transformers are tuned to 456 kilocycles. Set the signal-selector switch to "Mod. R.F.", the Modulation Control to "30%", the Band Selector to "B", and R.F. Control-1 and R.F. Control-2 to zero. Connect the coaxial cable of the signal generator to the cable connector marked "Low". Connect the black clip of this cable to the chassis of the receiver and the red clip to pin #4 of V_2.

Set the dial of the generator so that the red line coincides with 456 kilocycles on Band B. Turn up R.F. Control-1 and R.F. Control-2 until a 400-cycle whistle is heard in the loudspeaker and a significant reading appears on the output meter. (It may be necessary to select a lower range to get this reading.)

You will note that each intermediate-frequency transformer has two holes in the top of its can through which you can see the slotted heads of machine screws. These screws adjust the trimmer capacitors associated with their transformers. Using a slender, insulated screwdriver, adjust one of these screws of transformer T_2 for maximum reading on the output meter. Now adjust the other screw for the same result. Repeat the adjustment of the first screw. This completes the alignment of T_2.

Remove the red clip of the coaxial cable from pin #4 of V_2 and connect it to pin #8 of V_1. The reading of the output meter should increase. (Watch to see that the needle does not go off-scale, and select a higher range, if necessary.) Repeat the alignment procedure for transformer T_1. Then repeat the alignment of T_2.

(If these transformers are very much out of alignment at the start, it may be difficult to get a signal through. In that case, shift the coaxial cable from the "Low" to the "High" connector. If a still stronger signal is necessary, try turning up the Modulation Control. Except in the above case, the signal injected into the receiver should be kept at the lowest level that will give a significant reading on the meter. This is to avoid interference with the alignment procedure from the AVC system of the receiver.)

The next step is to line up the oscillator so that it will track with the incoming signal. With the red clip of the coaxial cable still connected to pin #8 of V_1, turn the Band Selector to "C" and set both the dial of the generator and the dial of the receiver to 1700 kilocycles. Adjust trimmer C_{2T} for maximum output on the meter. Set the dial of the generator and the dial of the receiver to 600 kilocycles. Repeat for maximum output. Repeat the procedure at 1700 kilocycles.

The final step consists of lining up the loop antenna. Attach both the black and red clips of the coaxial cable to the cardboard form upon which the loop antenna is wound. (The clips are placed near, but do not touch, the wire of the loop.) Set both the dial of the generator and the dial of the receiver to 1500 kilocycles. Adjust trimmer C_{1T} for maximum output on the meter.

This completes the alignment procedure. Disconnect the signal generator and output meter. Tune in the various stations, making a note of the position on the dial at which each station is received.

PROJECT #10

CODE
OSCILLATOR

REFERENCES

Elements of Radio, 3rd Edition. Pages 621-632.

Radio Servicing, 2nd Edition. Pages 333-368.

GENERAL INFORMATION

This project is an audio-frequency oscillator that, when the key is closed, produces an audible note in the loudspeaker. In this way it may be used as a code-learning device. The Morse code appears in Appendix 3 at the end of this book.

The 117L7-GT tube (V) is a multiunit type consisting of a beam power pentode and a half-wave rectifier in the same envelope. The pentode section is used to generate the audio signal. The rectifier section rectifies the line voltage to furnish the B voltage for the oscillator section. Because the heater of the tube can operate directly from the 117-volt line, no filament transformers or dropping resistors are required.

Note that the common negative lead for capacitors C_4 and C_5 connects to the line. Accordingly, if shock is to be avoided, the metal can should not be the common negative. Instead, electrolytic capacitors with separate negative leads should be used.

By throwing the toggle of switch S_2 to one side or the other, the tone of the output note can be made treble or bass. Potentiometer R_1 controls the volume of the output.

CODE OSCILLATOR

65

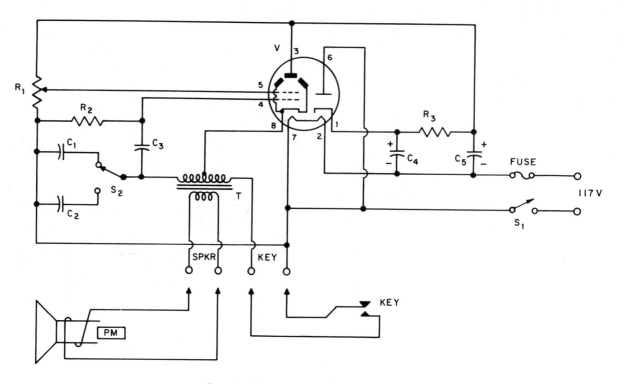

Circuit Diagram for Project No. 10

APPARATUS AND MATERIALS REQUIRED

C_1—0.1-μf fixed capacitor, 400 v DCW (tubular-paper type)

C_2—0.01-μf fixed capacitor, 400 v DCW (tubular-paper type)

C_3—0.05-μf fixed capacitor, 400 v DCW (tubular-paper type)

C_4
C_5 } Dual 10-10-μf electrolytic capacitor, 150 v DCW. Separate negative leads

R_1—50K-ohm potentiometer (volume control) with SPST switch (S_1) mounted on rear

R_2—30K-ohm, ½ watt, fixed resistor

R_3—500-ohm, 10 watt, wire-wound fixed resistor

S_1—Single-pole, single-throw, switch mounted on rear of volume-control potentiometer (R_1)

S_2—Single-pole, double-throw, rotary switch (tone control)

T—Output transformer, center-tapped primary, secondary for 4-ohm voice coil

V—117L7-GT rectifier-beam power amplifier tube

1 Loudspeaker, permanent-magnet dynamic type, mounted in wall baffle. Diameter 6", voice coil 4 ohms, 3½ watts

1 Telegraph key

1 Fuse holder, for type 8AG fuse

1 Fuse, type 8AG, 1 ampere

1 Octal socket

2 Small knobs

4 Tip jacks (banana type) 2 red, 2 black

4 Tip plugs (banana type) 2 red, 2 black

1 Male outlet plug

6 feet line cord (two leads)

Chassis 6" x 5¼" x 1½"

Miscellaneous hardware (2 single tie lugs, woodscrews, machine bolts, nuts, washers).

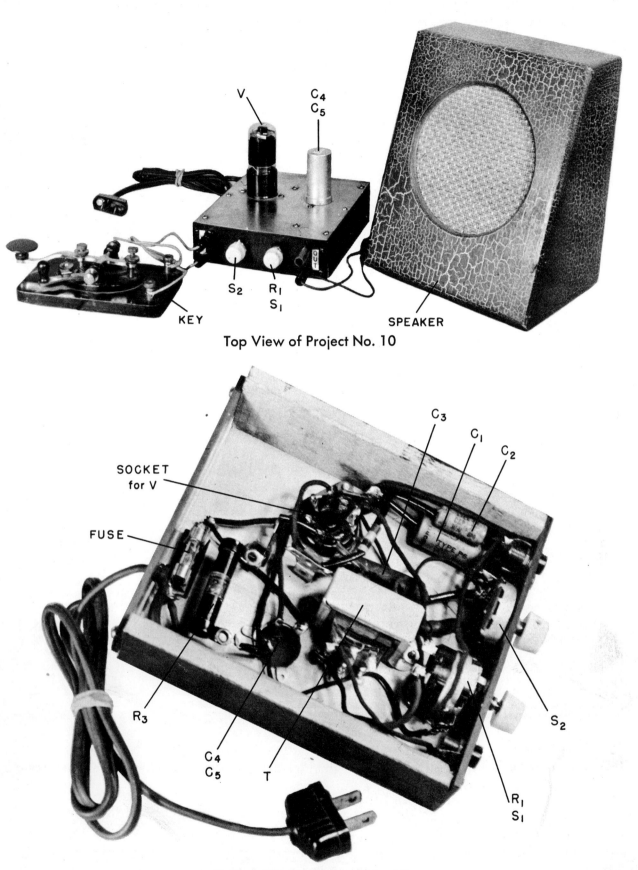

V C₄ C₅

C₄ / C₅ labels: C_4 C_5

KEY

S₂ R₁ S₁

SPEAKER

Top View of Project No. 10

SOCKET for V

FUSE

C₃ C₁ C₂

S₂

R₃

C₄ C₅ T

R₁ S₁

Bottom View of Project No. 10

CODE OSCILLATOR

COMPONENTS USED IN THIS PROJECT

Symbol

Explanation

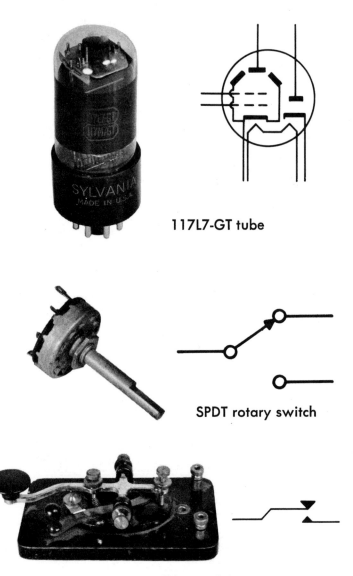

117L7-GT tube

SPDT rotary switch

Telegraph key

The 117L7-GT tube consists of a beam power amplifier and a half-wave rectifier contained in a single envelope. The heater operates directly from the 117-volt line.

Pin #1 is the rectifier cathode. Pin #2 is one end of the heater. Pin #3 is the amplifier plate. Pin #4 is the control grid of the amplifier. Pin #5 is the amplifier screen grid. Pin #6 is the rectifier plate. Pin #7 is the other end of the heater. Pin #8 is the amplifier cathode.

Rotation of the shaft connects the arm of the switch (as indicated by the arrow) to one or the other of the two contacts.

The telegraph key is a switch that is used to open or close a circuit. When the key is pressed down, the circuit is closed. When the pressure on the key is released, a spring forces the lever up, opening the circuit.

CONSTRUCTION

Examine the photographs of the project to plan your layout of components, keeping in mind that leads (especially plate and grid leads) should be as short as possible. Sketch your proposed layout on a sheet of paper and show it to your instructor for his approval.

Center-punch all holes and drill them. Mount all components on the chassis. Make a copy of the circuit diagram on a separate sheet of paper and, as you make the connections between components as indicated by the circuit diagram, mark each connection with a colored pencil.

If the output transformer (T) is of the universal type with more than two secondary taps, temporarily connect any two taps to the tip jacks for the voice coil of the loudspeaker. Later, during the testing procedure, shift these two leads around to find the two taps that produce the loudest signal in the loudspeaker.

TESTING AND OPERATION

Check your wiring to see that all connections have been made properly. Also check each soldered joint. Then show your project to your instructor for his approval.

Insert the tube into its socket and connect the loudspeaker and telegraph key to their respective tip jacks. Leave the key open. See that the fuse is in its holder. Insert the plug into the power outlet and throw switch S_1 to its "on" position. Allow a few minutes for the tube to warm up.

Close the telegraph key. You should hear a note in the loudspeaker. Turn the volume control (R_1) clockwise. The note should increase in volume. If the volume control is reversed, disconnect the oscillator from the power outlet and transpose the leads to the two outside terminals of the volume-control potentiometer (R_1).

If the secondary of transformer T has more than two taps, select the two that produce the loudest volume. Be sure to disconnect the oscillator from the power outlet whenever you make any changes.

Throwing the toggle of switch S_2 to one side or the other makes the note treble or bass. Select the tone most pleasing to you.

COLOR CODE
FOR MICA CAPACITORS

Most fixed capacitors have their values stamped on them. The mica-type capacitors, however, generally are color-coded. Unfortunately, there is a good deal of confusion in this coding, with different manufacturers using different codes. Most commonly, however, two types of codes are employed.

One is a three-dot code that is applied to mica capacitors rated at 500 volts, DCW. The color of the first dot indicates the first significant figure, that of the second dot the second significant figure, and that of the third dot indicates the multiplier. The value is read in micromicrofarads ($\mu\mu$f), and the sequence of the dots is indicated by an arrow.

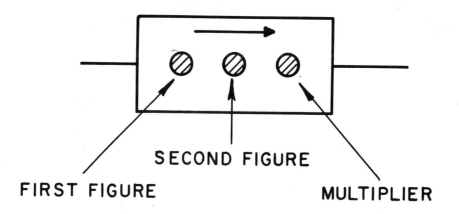

SECOND FIGURE

FIRST FIGURE   MULTIPLIER

If, for example, the first dot is red (which stands for 2), the second green (5), and the third brown (10), the value of the capacitor is 250 $\mu\mu$f or 0.00025 μf. (The table shown below indicates the numerical value of each color.)

The second code is a six-dot code that was drawn up by the electronic industry and is known as the RETMA code. To read this code, hold the capacitor with the arrow pointing to the right. The top left dot always will be white, to indicate that the standard RETMA code for mica capacitors is being employed. The top middle dot indicates the first significant figure and the top right indicates the second significant figure. The bottom right dot indicates the multiplier. As before, values are read in micromicrofarads. The bottom middle dot indicates the tolerance of the capacitor—that is, the permissible deviation from its rated value. The bottom left dot indicates the classification of the capacitor—that is, certain special electrical characteristics.

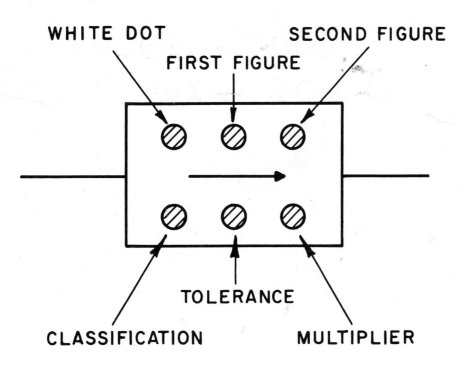

WHITE DOT   SECOND FIGURE

FIRST FIGURE

CLASSIFICATION   MULTIPLIER

TOLERANCE

The working-voltage ratings of the capacitors vary with the capacitance in accordance with specifications worked out by the RETMA committee.

KEY TO COLOR CODE

Color	Sig. Figure	Multiplier	Tolerance	Classification
Black	0	1	± 20%	A
Brown	1	10		B
Red	2	100	± 2%	C
Orange	3	1000	± 3%	D
Yellow	4	10000		
Green	5		± 5%	
Blue	6			
Violet	7			
Gray	8			I
White	9			J
Gold		0.1		
Silver		0.01	± 10%	

COLOR CODE FOR FIXED RESISTORS

For the purpose of identifying the values of fixed resistors, a color code, known as the RMA color code, is employed. Three colors are used to indicate the resistance, in ohms, of the resistor. A fourth color may be used to indicate the percentage tolerance of the resistor—that is, the permissible deviation from the rated resistance.

KEY TO RMA COLOR CODE

Color	1st Figure	2nd Figure	Multiplier	Tolerance
Black	—	0	1	
Brown	1	1	10	1%
Red	2	2	100	2%
Orange	3	3	1,000	3%
Yellow	4	4	10,000	4%
Green	5	5	100,000	
Blue	6	6	1,000,000	
Purple	7	7	10,000,000	
Gray	8	8	100,000,000	
White	9	9	1,000,000,000	
Silver				10%
Gold				5%
no color				20%

In old-type resistors, the first color, which represents the first significant figure, was the color of the *body* of the resistor. The second color, which represents the second significant figure, was the color of the *tip* of the resistor. The third color, which represents the multiplier, was a *dot,* usually at the center of the resistor.

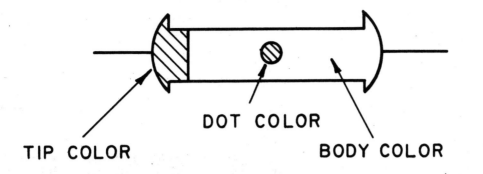

DOT COLOR

TIP COLOR   **BODY COLOR**

For example, if the body were brown, the tip green, and the dot yellow, the value of the resistor would be 150,000 ohms.

In present-day resistors, these colors usually are shown in bands, with the first band being the one nearest to one end. Sometimes a fourth band, indicating the tolerance, appears on the resistor.

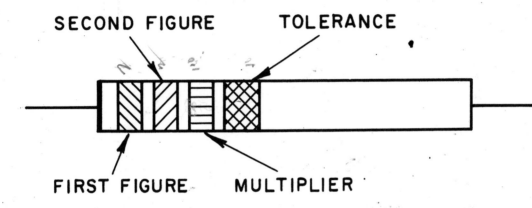

SECOND FIGURE   **TOLERANCE**

FIRST FIGURE   **MULTIPLIER**

Incidentally, when indicating the value of resistors, the letter K stands for thousands and the letter M stands for millions of ohms. Thus, for example, 15K ohms indicates 15,000 ohms, and 4.7M ohms indicates 4,700,000 ohms.

INTERNATIONAL MORSE CODE

This code consists of combinations of dots and dashes. The dots and the spaces between the dots and dashes are of equal duration. The dashes are three times as long.

A	.—	J	.———	S	...
B	—...	K	—.—	T	—
C	—.—.	L	.—..	U	..—
D	—..	M	——	V	...—
E	.	N	—.	W	.——
F	..—.	O	———	X	—..—
G	——.	P	.——.	Y	—.——
H	....	Q	——.—	Z	——..
I	..	R	.—.		

1	.————	6	—....
2	..———	7	——...
3	...——	8	———..
4	....—	9	————.
5	.....	0	—————

Period	.—.—.—	Wait	.—...
Interrogation	..——..	End of message	.
Break	—...—	End of transmission	...—.—